英汉对照

美国抒情诗100首

黄杲炘 译　俞亢咏 注

上海译文出版社

译诗的进化：
英语诗汉译百年回眸

（代序）

据钱钟书先生所见,最早译成汉语的英语诗,是美国诗人朗费罗(1807—1887)传诵一时的作品《人生颂》(1838)。译者是曾任上海江海关税务司的英国人威妥玛(1818—1895),此人在华期间编过汉语课本《语言自迩集》,设计拉丁字母拼写汉字,回英国后曾任剑桥大学汉语教授,可见对汉语还是有研究的。下面请看朗氏此诗的头两节原作及这位翻译官出身的威氏译文：

> Tell me not, in mournful numbers,
>> Life is but an empty dream!
> For the soul is dead that slumbers,
>> And things are not what they seem.

> Life is real! Life is earnest!
>> And the grave is not its goal;
> Dust thou art, to dust returnest,
>> Was not spoken of the soul.

勿以忧时言①
人生若虚梦
性灵睡即与死无异
不仅形骸尚有灵在

人生世上行走非虚生也总期有用
何谓死埋方至极处

---

① 钱氏认为,"时"当为"诗"字之误。

圣书所云人身原土终当归土

此言人身非谓灵也

以前似乎读到过一种说法,主张译诗分两步走:先由精通外语者将原作译出,然后再由诗人将之转化为诗。很巧的是,对上面这首英语诗正是这样做的,而完成其第二步的是当时的户部尚书董恂,他根据威氏的初译,"裁"成了下面的七绝:

莫将烦恼著诗篇　　　　天地生材总不虚

百岁原如一觉眠　　　　由来豹死尚留皮

梦短梦长同是梦　　　　纵然出土仍归土

独留真气满坤乾　　　　灵性常存无绝期

英语诗汉译,或者说外国诗汉译,就这样开了个头。这个头开得很怪,因为对威氏来说,这是将他的母语诗译为外语诗,译成非常难学的汉语和汉诗,这颇为少见。但威氏大概知道汉语中有五言诗,所以头两行译文也是五言的,只是随即放弃了这种追求,这或许与第三、四行是复合句有关。再看董氏的译文,尽管他依凭的初译者无疑精通英语,但其两节七言诗中似乎只有第二行与原作的含义相近。

威氏、董氏都是官场人物,译诗对他们而言,都是偶一为之,也许倒是"外事活动"的成分多一些。至少在董恂这方面不是不问青红皂白拿来就译的,他身为清王朝部级高官,当然很注意作品的"思想性",只是在看了威妥玛译文,"阅其语皆有警策意,无碍理者,乃允所请。"

这英语诗汉译第一例再清楚不过地告诉我们,译诗是一项颇具自己特点的工作,不管译者有什么身分、头衔,不管他们在外语和母语诗歌上多有修养,都难以保证这种合作的质量。看来,这样的译文还不能算是真正意义上的文学翻译。

从文学翻译的角度看,最早的英语诗汉译出现在上一个世纪之交。因为严复在1898年出版的《天演论》中译有英国诗人蒲柏(1688—1744)《人论》的片断,如:

元宰有秘机,斯人特未悟;

世事岂偶然,彼苍审措注。

> 乍疑乐律乖,庸知各得所?
> ……

和丁尼生(1809—1892)《尤利西斯》的片断,如:

> 挂帆沧海,风波茫茫;
> 或沦无底,或达仙乡。
> ……

一

　　严复的译诗还带有一点偶然因素,因为那部学术原作中引用了这些诗句,自当一并译出。但接下来的情况可说是:因为原作是诗,所以才特意译它。根据当时我国的国情,英国投身于希腊独立运动的浪漫主义诗人拜伦(1788—1824)特别受到国人的注意。他的长诗《唐璜》中的一段《哀希腊》,在 20 世纪初的十来年间,我国竟有四位最有声望的学人对之作了部分或全部译介。

　　《哀希腊》总共十六节,每节六行,每行是构成四个抑扬格音步的八个音节,六行诗的韵式为 ababcc。下面我们以其第一节为例,来看各家译文。请先读原作:

> The isles of Greece! the isles of Greece!
> 　　Where burning Sappho loved and sung,
> Where grew the arts of war and peace,
> 　　Where Delos rose, and Phoebus sprung!
> Eternal summer gilds them yet,
> But all, except their sun, is set.

　　1902 年,梁启超出版其小说《新中国未来记》,其中有他译的拜伦诗片断,包括这一节,其译文形式是类似"沉醉东风"的曲牌:

> 咳! 希腊啊,希腊啊!
> 你本是和平时代的爱娇,
> 你本是战争时代的天骄。
> 撒芷波歌声高,女诗人热情好,

更有那德罗士、菲波士荣光常照。
此地是艺文旧垒，技术中潮。
即今在否，算除却太阳光线，
万般没了。

1905年冬，马君武以七言歌行的形式译出全部十六节，其中的第一节为：

> 希腊岛，希腊岛，　　诗人沙浮安在哉？
> 爱国之诗传最早。　　战争平和万千术，
> 其术皆自希腊出。　　德娄、飞布两英雄，
> 溯源皆是希腊族。　　吁嗟乎！
> 漫说年年夏日长，　　万般销歇剩斜阳。

其后，有"天才文学家"之称的苏曼殊以五言古诗形式译出此诗（一说黄侃译），收在其《拜伦诗选》中。这第一节译文为：

> 巍巍希腊都，生长奢浮好。
> 情文何斐亹，荼幅思灵保。
> 征伐和亲策，陵夷不自葆。
> 长夏仍滔滔，颓阳照空岛。

1913年，胡适在美国读到马、苏两人对此诗的译文，"颇嫌君武失之讹，而曼殊失之晦，讹则失真，晦则不达……一夜，以四小时之力，译之。既成复改削数月"，后收入《尝试集》中。他以骚体译出的此诗第一节为：

> 嗟汝希腊之群岛兮，
> 实文教武术之所肇始，
> 诗媛沙浮尝咏歌于斯兮，
> 亦羲和、素娥之故里。
> 今惟长夏之骄阳兮，
> 纷灿烂其如初，
> 我徘徊以忧伤兮，
> 哀旧烈之无馀！

以上四种译文虽形式各异，格律有严有宽，用词或古奥或平易，而且胡适还是有意为马译、苏译"纠偏"的，却无一例外地具有

两个特征。一是形式均属于我国古典诗歌范畴,与原作形式无关,连行数都与原作的不同。二是用的都为文言,读来让人感到我国传统诗中古色古香的情调,缺乏与口语相去不远的原作风味。之所以会如此,是因为就诗歌而言,重要的不仅是说了些什么,而且是以什么方式说的。所以,既然使用的是我国传统诗中的句式和词汇,得到的也就不外是这样的效果。

说来也是历史的必然或局限。我国最早的这些译诗先驱,都是国学根底深厚的饱学之士,在他们的心目中,传统诗的形式是诗的当然载体。于是,他们在刚开始译诗时,信手拈来的形式、句式和词汇自然是他们最熟悉的东西。即使是另几位最杰出的大师如林纾、王国维和鲁迅,他们的译诗也同样有此倾向。

上面四种译文里,梁译的形式还是相当自由的,但他仍然认为:"本篇以中国调译外国意,填谱选韵,在在窒碍,万不能尽如原意。"胡适的译文虽更加自由,但这种骚体读来读去,只觉得像峨冠博带的老夫子在吟哦凭吊,不像意气风发的英国青年浪漫诗人在慷慨高歌。

对这类情况,研究中国古典文学和近代文学的郭延礼先生的结论是:"读这些译诗,均有'似曾相识'之感。翻译外国诗歌用中国古典诗体,又用文言,很难成功。"(《中国近代翻译文学概论》101页。)这个结论客观而中肯。从实际情况看,尽管这种译诗在我国历史最悠久,但迄今为止,除了一些较短小的抒情诗,似乎还未曾见过有谁以这种方式去译英美诗中的大作品,尤其是现代作品,这可以说明其适应性极其有限。再说,即使是译抒情诗,一百年来的成果也不多;即使偶有成功的,流传也不广。毕竟,翻译的目的是为了介绍原作的真实面貌,所以时至今日,如果有谁想通过译文去了解某一名作,那么只要有其它译本可供选择,哪怕是散文译本,他就多半不会首先选择这类"似曾相识"的。由此可见,译诗要另觅途径势在必行。

二

事实上,不要说是译诗,即使是创作诗,这时也要突破我国的传统诗形式了。当然这两者之间有关联且互为因果。明显的例子是胡适,他于 1913 年(一说 1914 年 2 月)译了《哀希腊》,1916 年则已首先在尝试用白话写诗,过后又用白话译诗了。他1920年出版的我国第一部个人新诗《尝试集》中,像外国一些诗人那样也收有译诗,其中两首以旧体文言诗形式译出,包括《哀希腊》。另外三首则译成白话新诗,而且他把这三首译作包括在他自认为最重要的,可真正称为白话新诗的十四首作品中。下面请看其译于1919年2月的其中最短一首——据徐志摩说,"那是他最得意的一首译诗,也是在他诗里最'脍炙人口'的一首。"下面是胡适依据的原作及其译文:

Ah! Love, could you and I with Him Conspire

To grasp this sorry Scheme of things entire,

Would not we shatter it to bits—and then

Remould it nearer to the Heart's Desire!

要是天公换了卿和我,

该把这糊涂世界一齐都打破,

要再磨再炼再调和,

好依着你我的安排,把世界重新造过。

此诗原作出自一本篇幅极小,而译本及版本之多可谓世界之最的诗集《柔巴依集》。1922年,郭沫若根据英国菲氏《柔巴依集》第四版,译出并发表了全部译文。也许郭沫若不知道,Rubai这种诗体本就是我国维吾尔、乌兹别克、哈萨克等少数民族文学中的传统诗体,在汉语中约定俗成的译名为"柔巴依",所以他才称之为《鲁拜集》。看来,这既是我国现代文学翻译史上第一部完整译出的抒情诗集,也是第一本以新诗形式译出的诗集。郭译的此诗为:

啊,爱哟! 我与你如能串通"他"时,

把这不幸的"物汇规模"和盘攫取,

怕你我不会把它捣成粉碎——

我们从新又照着心愿抟拟!

这首译诗最早发表时,首行文字与这里的不同。但闻一多细读了全部集子后,写了篇也许是我国最早译诗批评的长文《莪默伽亚谟之绝句》,既作热情评价,也直率指出多处误译,例如郭把这首行中的with Him conspire误解成为against Him conspire。于是郭译作了改正。闻一多还指出:此首的"胡(适)译虽过于自由,毫未依

傍原文,然而精神尚在。"同时,他也译了此诗:

> 爱哟! 你我若能和"他"勾通好了,
> 将这全体不幸的世界攫到,
> 我们怕不要捣得他碎片纷纷,
> 好依着你我的心愿去再抟再造!

这里我们可以回头看一下这首诗原作的格律:四行诗的长度均为十音节,构成五个抑扬格音步(这是英诗中最常见的诗行),韵式为 aaba。正是这几点构成了英语中柔巴依这种诗体。再看前面三种译文。胡译毫未依傍原文,结果各行字数和顿数相差很大,最长与最短行差了近一倍。而与原作内容比较对得拢的郭译与闻译中,各行长度就比较匀称,字数都在十一到十三之间,而顿数则绝大多数为五。

这个随机的例子表明,如表达的是同一个意思,那么英语和现代汉语的句子长度是相近的,或者说,现代汉语中的"顿"与英诗中的"音步"在"容量"上是大致相当的。① 可惜 1924 年时,徐志摩只是比照着胡(适)译,提供其徐译如下:

> 爱啊,假如你我能勾着运神谋反,
> 一把抓住了这整个儿"寒尘"②的世界,
> 我们还不趁机会把他完全捣烂——
> 再按我们的心愿,改造他一个痛快?

四行诗虽较胡译匀称,但字数多了不少,主要是因为增加了一些原作中"查无实据"的词,如"一把"、"趁机会"和"一个痛快"。但徐译第一行中用"运神"而不用"他"却是有根据的,因为徐译依据的版本中这里用的不是 Him,而是同样单音节的 Fate。

距胡适译《哀希腊》不过十来年时间,包括胡适在内的这四位文化界巨擘在译同一首诗时,竟无一例外地译成了白话自由诗!这当然不是他们对祖国传统诗歌形式感情不深,或者他们没有能

---

① 这个问题和类似问题已在其它拙文中作了较仔细的讨论。本文中或顺便再举出个例子,或简单地引用一下结论。有兴趣探讨的读者可参阅拙作《从柔巴依到坎特伯雷——英语诗汉译研究》(湖北教育版,1999 年 11 月)。

② 寒尘一作寒伧。——原注

力将此诗译成那类形式。造成这一奇特现象的,一方面固然有时代潮流的影响:白话文兴起后,写诗、译诗也随之用了白话文,原来适用于文言的诗体、诗律自然就被突破,而适合于白话的诗律一时又未建立,因此对于有必要照应原作内容的译诗而言,自然只能让其以自由诗的形式存在了。另一方面,用白话文译诗自有其合理性,因为至少在英语诗中,诗歌语言与口语的差别远没有汉语文言诗与口语的这么大,对说英语的人而言,几乎任何英语诗都是能听明白的——在此情况下,用白话文去译自然比用文言更容易使译文比较接近原作。这也就是为什么曾经也用文言译过外国诗的徐志摩后来放弃了这种尝试,转而极力主张用白话译诗。因为他根据实践已经发现:"旧诗格所不能表现的意致的声调,现在还在草创时期的新体即使不能满意的,至少可以约略的传达。"①

对照《哀希腊》的四种译文就可看出,上列柔巴依的四种译文尽管都很自由,但总的来说,它们与原作比较接近,而且它们之间的差异远小于《哀希腊》四种译文间的差异,具有明显的可比性。道理很简单。《哀希腊》的几种译法里,译者完全无视原作的格律形式,只是根据他们想赋予其译诗的形式去"处理"或改造原作内容。而在白话自由诗的译法中,形式基本上是开放的或随意的,这自然有利于提高译文内容的保真度。

四位新诗人在二十年代前后的译诗一概都是白话自由体,这绝非偶然,而是译诗发展的必由之路。但是当时的有些情况可能也促成了此事。首先我们可以看一下:胡适十九岁赴美留学,在美国从1910年待到1917年,这段时间正是英美诗坛上意象派最活跃的阶段,而且,标志着美国新诗运动出发点的《诗刊》创刊于1912年,在接下来的二三年里,芝加哥诗派的重要人物桑德堡和马斯特斯又发表了引起很大反响的代表作——而这两派的诗作绝大多数是自由诗。

————

① 引自《征译诗启》。顺便说一下,尽管徐志摩"译诗里失败借鉴有余,成功榜样不多"(卞之琳语),但他为了组织译诗队伍,"从认真的翻译研究中国文字解放后表现致密的思想与有法度的声调与音节之可能,研究这新发现的达意的工具究竟有什么程度的弹性与柔韧性与一般的应变性……"他联络了郑振铎、胡适等人,在报上发表著名的《征译诗启》,准备"提出五六首短诗",请文艺爱好者"做一番更认真的译诗的尝试",以便"共同研究"。另外,他曾根据歌德一首短诗和卡莱尔的英译,作了一译再译并集中了胡适、郭沫若等人的另五种汉译,在报上加以比较和讨论,叙述了别人与他的观点;还在报上辟一《诗镌》,发表新诗及刊载译诗。这种为促进译诗发展而作的努力值得称赞。

胡适在美学习的固非文学或诗学,但不可能不感受到英美诗坛这股新的风气,从而"尝试"写白话新诗,继而又以白话文译诗。

再看其他三位:郭沫若 1914 年二十二岁时赴日学医;徐志摩 1918 年二十二岁时去美、英,先后学的是社会学、政治学、经济学;闻一多 1922 年二十三岁时去美国学美术。他们四人看到的既然是日益增多的英美自由诗,这自然会产生耳濡目染的效果,而他们非文学专业的学习也未必会使他们在译诗之前就对英语诗的格律了然于心。

其实这种情况并不少见。我就是在不知英诗格律为何物之时开始译诗的。这很自然,因为读诗不一定需要格律知识,读到哪一首突然来了兴趣或有了感悟,随手就凭感觉译了出来。偶尔凭兴趣译些诗歌的,恐怕都很少先钻研一番原文的诗律。译了多本诗集的仍可能对原文的诗律不甚了了。当然也有懂得原作格律的,但"自由诚可贵",一时难于放弃把格律诗译成自由诗的自由。而且,既然大师们也这样译,那就不妨照此办理。于是,把格律诗当自由诗译就成了普遍现象,并在广大读者中造成了错觉:原来外国诗都是自由诗。而大量涌现的白话自由诗又似乎反过来证明这种译诗存在的合理性。

三

然而,即使不谈诗歌格律的审美意义和表意功能,不谈它反映诗歌民族性、时代性、诗歌内容倾向和诗人风格的功能,把格律诗译成无格律诗也是令人十分遗憾的。格律诗是内容与形式完美结合的产物,可谓珠联璧合,浑然一体。一首或一节英语格律诗,看它的诗行数、各诗行的长短和性质及押韵方式,就可确定该诗的格律特性,就可在英诗格律体系的"坐标"上将其定位。如果此诗译成汉语后,只剩下内容而没有了格律,那么它将游离在英诗的格律体系之外(格律中蕴含的信息受到损失),无法通过格律同其它格律诗作纵向与横向的比较。可以说,失却了格律的译诗是跛脚的,是行之不远的。

即使上面这些都撇开不谈,只凭我们是一个具有悠久格律诗传统的民族,人们就不会满足于自由诗。就连上面几位写新诗的代表人物也尝试过写格律新诗,如胡适的《梦与诗》(1920)、郭沫若的

《Venus》(1919)、闻一多的《死水》(1925)和徐志摩的《渺小》(1931)等等。只是他们的这种尝试和探索似乎没有延伸到译诗中去。

看来,在较早的白话译诗中进行格律化尝试的是朱湘。明显的例子就是他选译的十五首柔巴依,包括译上面的那首:

> 爱呀! 要是与命运能以串通,
> 拿残缺的宇宙把握在掌中,
> 我与你便能捧碎了——又抟起,
> 抟成了如意的另一个穹隆!

朱湘这十五首译诗有两个共同点,即四行诗的韵式都为 aaba,与原作的一致;每行诗的长度都为十一字,与原作每行的十个音节相当接近。朱湘这种按字数建行的做法其实也很自然,因为在我国传统的文言诗中,诗行长短是以字为单位而计量的,字数的整齐往往就意味着节奏的整齐,于是这种观念与做法也就被带进了白话诗。

当然,译文用十一个汉字的诗行应原作十音节诗行只是这种尝试之一,实践中并不普遍。较常见的倒是以十二个汉字的译文应原作的十音节诗行,其最著名的例子可数梁宗岱译的《莎士比亚十四行诗集》——其中几乎所有的诗行都为十二字。另外,朱湘本人也常用十个汉字诗行译十音节的英语诗行,这样做的还有柏丽等人。请看柏丽于 1990 年发表的对上面那首柔巴依的译文:

> 啊,我爱! 愿咱与命运商讨,
> 抓住这万物的糟糕图稿!
> 怎不把这世界捣成碎片? ——
> 好按我们心愿重抟再造!

在英语诗汉译史上,朱湘的这种实践有相当重要的意义。因为这种译法首先有意识地尝试了以具有某种格律形式的译诗去反映原作的格律,对原作的格律形式采取了同样的负责态度,用他认为合适的量化的汉语(十一个字)去反映用量化的英语(十个音节)写成的诗。可以看出,在这种译诗标准里,译文诗行中的量化单位是字。①

---

① 由于法语格律诗大多纯由音节建行,这种译法已可满足反映原作形式的要求,所以特别有意义,而法语诗汉译者中,采用这种译法的也就较多。

四

上面说过,早在新诗出现之初,一些诗人已在尝试写格律新诗,并由此注意到格律新诗的建行单位不应是单字而应当是音组或顿,然后将这一受西洋格律诗中"音步"的启发而创建的建行单位反过来再用于译格律诗。于是,孙大雨在三十年代初,卞之琳在五十年代中译莎士比亚诗剧时,有意识地以含有五音组或顿的汉语诗行来反映原作的五音步诗行。在现在的英诗汉译中,这种被称为"以顿代步"的译诗要求已获得突出的成就和广泛的影响。例如屠岸的《莎士比亚十四行诗集》和杨德豫的《拜伦诗七十首》便是这种译法的著名范例,单看它们数十万册的印数,便可得知它们受人喜爱的程度。

不巧的是,尽管《柔巴依集》是我国译本最多的诗集,但迄今仍未看到纯按"以顿代步"要求译出的,只是在某些比较自由的译文中有时能发现几首恰好(这"恰好"也自有其必然性!)符合这种要求的译文,例如飞白译的这首就是:

> 爱人哟! 你我若能与他合谋,
> 抓起这大千世界的可悲结构,
> 我们岂不会把它砸个粉碎,
> 再重新塑造得更接近心的要求!

同上面限定诗行字数的译诗要求相比,这种"以顿代步"的要求似更合理一些,因为它限定的是译文中每行的顿数,要求这顿数与原作中的音步数一致,从而反映出可算原作最重要格律因素的诗行长短,而对绝大多数英语格律诗来说,诗行长短的计量单位是音步而不是音节,尽管音步是由音节构成的。而限定译诗诗行字数的做法,只是准确地或比较接近地反映原作诗行的音节数,却不是其音步数。例如朱湘的译文中,尽管每行以十一字应原作的十音节,但四行的顿数却分别为五、四、四、四——各行之间既有差异,与原作的音步数也不相同。

然而,也有人反对"以顿代步"这种做法。这里有两种情况。一种是要走"民族化"的路子,仍要用我国传统诗的形式去译外国诗。这方面的代表也许可算是丰华瞻,例如他在 1997 年 12 月 10

日《中华读书报》上发表的《谈译诗的"归化"》中,明确表示他"不赞成移植原诗的形式"。为什么不赞成呢?"以顿代步"的译诗要求有什么根本性缺陷吗?他没有说,只是讲:"移植英诗形式的效果并不理想。往往弄得句子很长,不便于诵读和流传。有的句子读起来相当别扭。"

这种笼而统之的说法让人产生一系列的问题。"民族化"译诗的效果理想吗?比移植形式的译诗理想?如果移植形式的译文中句子并不很长,读起来又不别扭,(丰先生的话中用了"往往"与"有的",说明不是没这种可能,至于说"流传",我倒想请问一下:"民族化"译诗流传到了什么程度呢?)那么丰先生是否就赞成移植形式的译法呢?下面我们就来看一节丰先生常用来作为例子出示的译诗及其原作:

> 晚钟殷殷响,夕阳已西沉。
> 群牛呼叫归,迂回走草径。
> 农夫荷锄犁,倦倦回家门。
> 惟我立旷野,独自对黄昏。

> The curfew tolls the knell of parting day,
> The lowing herd wind slowly o'er the lea,
> The ploughman homeward plods his weary way,
> And leaves the world to darkness and to me.

这是英国诗人格雷(1716—1771)的名篇《挽歌》中的第一节。这里,"民族化"的译法带来的表达和意象上的改变,节奏与情调上的差异,就不一一列举了。然而,用移植原作形式的译法似较可避免这些损失,请看下面的拙译:

> 晚钟敲起,为逝去的白昼送终;
> 牛群哞哞,在牧场上迤逦慢走;
> 耕夫回家,疲惫的脚步缓又重;
> 这个世界,就留给了我和昏幽。

这个译文中,每个实词在原作中都有依据,原作中每个实词在译文中也都得到落实,译文中既无增饰也无减损,更没有"掉包"的东西。这是合理的译诗要求带来的合理结果。再以丰先生的标准来看,这些句子恐也不能算长(尽管创作诗中也不乏长句),读起来也未必很别扭,那么丰先生赞成这样的移植吗?

我估计仍不会赞成的。

一个人爱读什么诗或爱写什么诗,这决定于他的情趣。但译者的职责是尽可能如实地反映原作面貌,是把原作内容与形式中蕴含的信息尽可能都传达出来。这要求译者感情和精力的投入,也要求译者有科学和理性的态度。毕竟,格律诗的形式与内容之间关系十分密切,与民族的文化传统之间关系也十分密切,因此,如果硬要把我们传统诗形式加在外国诗的内容上,那么除非把外国诗的内容改造得不像外国诗,否则,即使这种努力是认真的,其结果却往往是不和谐的,甚至是滑稽的——就像是让说相声的洋人穿着长衫或让洋妞的天然大脚穿我们的绣花小鞋。

当然,出于个人的爱好,一定要按这种"民族化"要求译诗也未尝不可,但若是要以此种要求来反对"以顿代步"的译法,那恐怕是不现实的,因为这两者不仅合理性不同,而且可行性也不一样,何况随着文言离我们越来越远,前者的可行性将越来越小。即以上面提到的丰文而言,文中举出的四个译例中已有两个"进化"到白话自由诗,[①] 例如所译莎士比亚十四行诗第 18 首的前四行:

> 可否把你比作明媚的夏天?
> 你比夏天更可爱,更温婉。
> 夏日会起狂风,把五月的苞蕾摧残;
> 好景能有几时,转眼花事阑珊。

其实,这节诗原作的格律与上面《挽歌》那节原作的格律完全相同。既然如此,为什么这诗不用"民族化"译法呢? 看来,要么是译者认为此诗用此译法不合适,要么就是用此译法而不成功。无论哪种情况,都只能证明这种译法的局限性。而一种主张连主张者在实践中都不能一以贯之,对别人还有什么说服力呢?

反对"以顿代步"的另一种情况,则是主张"用自由诗的格式"。例如劳陇先生于《中国翻译》1992 年第 5 期上发表的《我看英诗翻

---

① 在 1997 年出版的《丰华瞻译诗集》中,英诗汉译总共 19 首,但其中在译诗形式上真正做到"民族化"的,仅三四首而已。

译中的"以顿代步"问题》(下面简称《我》文)即持此种观点。那么反对的依据是什么呢?

该文首先引经据典地证明了一个常识:"节奏,必须具备两个条件:1.节拍均匀(即时距相等),2.抑扬有致(即轻重之分)。两者是缺一不可的。"其次又未加证明地下了个结论,说汉语"没有轻重音节之分,在诗中以'平仄'来表示'扬抑'。"

然后,该文提出这样几点:

1)"以顿代步"中,"每顿包含的音节不等,就不可能节拍均匀;音节不拘于平仄、轻重,也就没有抑扬之致……就不可能产生节奏感。"

2)举出卞之琳按"以顿代步"要求译出的《哈姆雷特》中五行诗并分顿如下:

|活下去|还是|不活:|这是|问题:|
|要做到|高贵|究竟该|忍气|吞声|①
|来容受|狂暴的|命运|矢石|交攻呢,|
|还是该|挺身|反抗|无边的|苦恼,|②
|扫它个|干净?|……

说是"每顿的音节参差不齐,又不讲轻重、平仄,无抑扬之致,实在读不出节奏感来"。

3)"英语中也有'顿'(pause)的,'顿'以词意分而不以音节分……在英语中,'顿'决不可以代替'音步'。怎么到了汉语之中,'顿'就成了'音步',而且还有节奏感呢?"

4)最后,文章又引经据典,强调"诗律不可译",说是"在诗歌翻译上,我们完全可以用自由诗的格式,因为译诗毕竟以内容为主,形式、格律是次要的。只要能贴切地传达原诗的意境、神韵,不应该受任何形式的束缚。"

其实,"顿"或者"音组"是否能构成节奏,是一个已被实践证明了的问题(理论上有孙大雨的文章《论音组》等),从二十年代起,很多诗人的大量作品已证明了这一点。但既然在《我》文作者这样的层次上这个问题仍未解决,看来有必要再耐心地作些说明。下面请看孙大雨有意用音组为节奏单位写的一首十四行诗首节(这首

---

① ②　如果是我朗诵,这两个"该"字似乎该划在后一个"顿"里。

发表在 1926 年 4 月 10 日的作品也许是我国最早有意识写出的格律新诗)：①

> 　　往常的天幕是顶无忧的华盖，
> 　　　　往常的大地永远任意地平张；
> 　　　　往常时摩天的山岭在我身旁
> 　　峙立，长河在奔腾，大海在澎湃；

　　这诗读起来有节奏吗？如果有，那么这节奏单位不可能是"字"，因为在白话里构成形容词与副词的"的"、"地"等等发音时一带而过，与其它"字"时距不等，所以节奏单位只能是往往由二字或三字构成的音组或顿。而如果读来没有节奏，那么建筑在同样基础上的大量格律诗，包括闻一多的《死水》，不也同样没有了节奏，不成其为诗了？所以，如果劳陇先生要证明音组或顿不是新诗的节奏单位，那么他最好先证明《死水》等等作品也没有节奏，要不，就请证明这些诗中另有什么除"字"之外的节奏单位。

　　这里我还想提一下"平仄"的问题。"平仄"虽可以加强诗句的节奏感，却不是构成节奏的必要条件。事实上，不讲究平仄的诗多得很，但它们照样有节奏，例如"关关雎鸠，在河之洲"就是。下面对劳陇先生所提各点分别加以说明。

　　1）每顿包含的音节通常为二三个，例如下面冯至的两行诗中，有四个两音节顿和四个三音节顿："有多少｜面容，｜有多少｜语声／在我们｜梦里｜是这般｜真切。"之所以音节数不同却能构成一个顿，是因为顿中各音节在发音时的轻重、长短是不一样的，②因此尽管音节数不全相同，仍有可能构成时距相当的顿。甚至在"哦，｜你曾经｜把惠特曼｜颂扬"这样的句子中，"哦"与"把惠特曼"的时距也大致相当，因为"哦"特别悠长，而后者则比较急促。我们还可以注意到，除"哦"以外的几个顿里，"曾"、"惠"、"颂"发音较重较长，而顿里其它字发音则相对较轻较短。这完全符合构成节奏的两个条件。

　　这里我想强调一点：诗歌中的"节拍均匀"并不像钟摆那样地

---

①　见孙大雨《格律体新诗的起源》（《文艺争鸣》1992 年第 5 期）。
②　可以说，即使在平时说话中，也没有一个人让他说的每个音节都在轻重和长短上一致。正因为如此，连说话中也可有抑扬顿挫。

机械,而是可根据内容与感情的需要而略有弹性的。这情形在英语诗中也一样,例如胡适早年还译过美国女诗人 Sara Teasdale (1884—1933)的一首 Over the Roofs,此诗首节原文为:

> I said,"I have shut my heart,
> As one shuts an open door,
> That Love may starve within
> And trouble me no more."

这节诗中的音步大多由一轻一重的两音节组成,每行都含三个音步。但第一行中的 I have shut 与第二行中的 As one shuts 都是由二轻一重的三音节构成的音步,却仍与二音节音步放在一起使用。另一方面,用一个重音音节顶一个两或三音节音步的情况也同样很常见,最著名的例子可见丁尼生(1809—1892)的这样两行诗:Break,break,break/On thy cold grey stones,O sea! 这里的第一行仅三个音节,另一行为七个音节,但它们都是三音步! 类似的情况英诗中多得很,可谓不胜枚举,这里就再讲一种更特别的"跳跃节律"吧。在霍普金斯(1844—1889)首创的这种节律里,一个音步可以是单单一个重音,也可以由一个重音带一个、两个、三个甚至四个非重音构成。

2) 读以顿建行的诗句,都可感受到其节奏。"读不出节奏感"的原因,不一定是诗句没有节奏。一个睡眼惺忪的小孩在勉强背诗,老和尚念经似地背道:"春眠不觉晓处处闻啼鸟",人们听来毫无节奏感,这能说诗没有节奏吗?

3) 英诗中的"顿"确实以词意分而不以音节分,且不能代替音步。这是因为英语词所含的音节数过于悬殊,且没有规律,所以英语诗若按"顿"建行,将很难保证"时距相等"。但汉语情况不同,现代汉语中的词基本上都是两音节的,因此按意义分的"顿"时距一致,具有构成节奏的基础,而一些附加上去的"的了呢吗"和"在就把为"等等都是虚词,在阅读中一带而过,并不怎么影响时距。

4) 诗律即使不可译,但译诗如果能反映一点原作诗行的长短或相对长短有什么不好呢? 上面那首柔巴依的几种译文里,那首符合"以顿代步"要求的译文在反映原作内容上非但没有不如四种自由诗译文,相反还有所提高。可见,对译诗形式提出要求是全面提高译诗质量的手段。如果因为不能准确地重现原作格律,就放弃可约略反映原作格律的机会,宁可在原地止步不前,这算什么逻辑呢?

诗歌是一种文学精品,格律诗是内容与格律形式并重的诗。在这里,形式并不是内容的"束缚",① 而是其恰如其分的合理载体。什么是神韵? 对我来说,格律诗的格律就是其神韵中的一个要素。一首格律诗连格律都不要了,还大谈什么神韵呢?②

五

"以顿代步"的译法当然并不是完美无缺的,它虽能反映原作诗行中的音步数,从而反映原作中各诗行音步数整齐或变化有序的情况,却未能反映原作中往往也是整齐或变化有序的诗行音节数情况。因此,一首这样的译诗尽管音步上整齐,音节上仍可能参差不齐,从而使不熟悉"顿"的读者未能看出这是一首格律诗。

与此相反,朱湘那种译法顾的是音节那一头,而由于汉语中的字即音节,因此一首诗行字数整齐的译诗在形式上就相当整齐,让人看来一目了然——尽管它"内部"的顿数是不整齐的。

那么,是不是有可能让译诗结合这两者的优点,兼顾译诗诗行中的顿数与字数呢? 回答是肯定的。根据我本人英语诗汉译约六万行的实践,这种可能是极大的。请看上述那首柔巴依的拙译:

> 爱人哪! 如果你我能同他协力,
> 把握这全部事物的可悲设计,

① 采用自由诗形式译诗,往往以"牺牲形式以保存内容"为理由,似乎忠实于内容与反映形式是完全矛盾的。但事实证明这两者是可以并行不悖的。相反,放弃了形式而想"贴切地传达原诗的意境、神韵",恐怕只是愿望而已。不妨设想一下:李白"床前明月光"诗中的这点内容如果没有形式把它凝聚起来,能流传到今天吗? 还有,自由诗形式的译文尽管铺天盖地,能具体地举出一些贴切传达了原作意境、神韵的例子吗?

② "神"这个字很抽象,很飘渺,很神秘。一幅人像画得不像,却可以说它是神似而非形似。其实,画不像是因为当时没掌握人体解剖知识或透视法,所以只能"神似"了。再说,一首格律诗的"神韵"能由自由诗传达出来的话,那么大概也能由散文传达了,是不是这样呢?

我们就不用先把它砸个粉碎，

再把它塑造得比较称心如意！

这里，每一行诗都是含五顿的十二字，既反映了原作每行五音步，又反映了原作中诗行音节数整齐的特点。也许有人会说，既然已经做到这个地步了，为什么不干脆都译成含五顿的十字诗行呢，那样岂不是同原作的十音节五音步完全对应起来了？对此，可简答如下：

1）英语诗中单音节词很多，例如上面原作中的四行诗共四十个音节，单音节词就有二十六个。而现代汉语中单音节词已很少用，因此译文即使注意精练，字数也往往略多于原作的音节数。说"略多"，是因为用英语或汉语表达同样内容时，所需的音节数在一般情况下是相当接近的。如果把上面从胡适到飞白的七种译文统计一下，就可发现每行的平均音节数为11.6，而每行的平均顿数为4.8——几乎就是十二字和五顿！

2）现代汉语中，形容词和副词等常由三字构成，有时还有四字顿（当然偶尔也有一字顿），因此十个字的诗行往往仅含四顿（可见上面柏丽译文）。

3）即使能够做到每行十字五顿，这做法也不太可取。因为这时诗中可能全部是两字顿（一首这么短的柔巴依就有二十个两字顿），这易于使整首诗的节奏显得单调和呆板。相反，如果一行诗由十二三字构成，那么这种诗行不仅较易容纳四字顿，而且行中的两字顿与三字顿的搭配方式也比较灵活多样，富于变化。

上面讲的当然都是一般情况，也即以两音节音步建行的诗。事实上，对于一些比较特殊的诗，还是有可能使译文诗行的字数与顿数同原作诗行的音节数与音步数完全相合的。请看拜伦一首名作的首节原文与拙译：

The Assyrian came down like the wolf on the fold,

And his cohorts were gleaming in purple and gold;

And the sheen of their spears was like stars on the sea,

When the blue wave rolls nightly on deep Galilee.

这亚述王冲过来像狼扑向羊，

> 他麾下的队伍紫莹莹闪金光；
> 那矛尖像星星在大海上闪烁——
> 当夜晚加利利海深深卷碧波。

原作中韵式为 aabb，每行含十二音节，构成四个多由轻、轻、重三个音节组成的音步。而拙译中每行均为十二字，都含一个两字顿，两个三字顿，一个四字顿，各种顿的搭配方式互有不同。

另外，对于下面这样的短诗，尽管它全由两音节音步构成，但由于它各行长度都有不同，倒不妨在译文中全用两字顿。请看美国女诗人克莱普西(1878—1914)独创的一种五行诗之一 November Night 原作及拙译：

> Listen…
> With faint dry sound,
> Like steps of passing ghost,
> The leaves, frost-crisp'd, break from the trees
> And fall.

> 听啊……
> 蜷脆霜叶
> 宛如游魂脚步，
> 带着枯声悄然离树
> 而下。

原作中各行的音步数依次为一二三四一，音节数为二四六八二。译文中各行的顿数与音节数悉依原作。

从上面这些例子已可看出，按这种"兼顾译诗诗行顿数与字数"的要求译出的诗具有图形性和建筑美，能让读者在阅读前就一目了然地知道一首译诗是否有格律，大致有什么样的格律。然而这只是"副产品"，更重要的是，这样的译诗能清楚地反映出原作格律并把按音步建行的各种格律不同的诗区分得明明白白，把蕴含在各种格律里的诗歌的民族性、时代性，诗的内容倾向，诗的某些特色(如图形诗等)及诗人的某种风格(如喜欢自创一格或用外国格律等)显示出来。

还不仅如此。把译诗要求推进到这一步以后，译者已可回过头来很方便地解决英语诗中其它节律的翻译问题,因为在英语诗中,以一个重音音节带一或二个轻音音节构成的音步建行并不是唯一的方式。例如斯宾塞(1552—1599)就尝试过另一种音步诗,在这种诗里,音步不按音节的轻重划分,而是像希腊、罗马和梵文等古典语言的诗歌中那样,按音节的长短来划分的。由于这种节律不很适合于英语诗,因此几乎不可能需要翻译,即使万一遇上,也可用"兼顾顿数与音节数"的要求去反映其音步与音节数,只要说明原作中音步构成的情况即可。

另一种节律就是前面提到过的霍普金斯的"跳跃节律"。这种节律里,音步数即重音数,而每个音步里的非重音数相差可以很悬殊。这种情况很像我们通常看到的某些常规音步诗,只是在这种诗里,音步中的非重音音节数不太固定,常有所增减。因此,这种诗可以用不管音节数的"以顿代步"去译。请看英国诗人梅斯菲尔德(1878—1967)名作 Sea-Fever 的首节与拙译:

I must go down to the seas again, to the lonely sea and the sky,
And all I ask is a tall ship and a star to steer her by,
And the wheel's kick and the wind's song and the white sail's shaking,
And a grey mist on the sea's face and a grey dawn breaking.

> 我得重下海去,去那寂寞的大海和长空;
> 我要的只是一艘高桅快船,一颗导航星,
> 只是海风的歌唱、白帆的颤栗、舵轮的倔强,
> 只是海面上灰蒙蒙的雾霭、灰蒙蒙的破晓曙光。

这原作是七音步诗,音步大多由一轻一重两音节构成。但第一行中有 to the seas、to the lone-和 and the sky 三个三音节音步,第二行中有 is a tall、and a star 两个三音节音步以及 ship 一个单音节音步……所以本诗尽管各诗行音步整齐,音节数却参差不齐。于是这里的译文各行中都为七顿,而音节数不限。

一些现代诗家则作过另一种尝试,即纯粹以音节建行,不考虑重音问题——当然,诗行中仍有重音,但只是按意义与修辞的需要而不规则地出现在诗行中,因此这种诗易被误认为自由诗。请看英国诗人冈恩(1929—　　　　)Blackie, the Electric Rembrandt 一诗首节及拙译:

We watch through the shop-front while
Blackie draws stars—an equal[①]

我们透过玻璃的店面
注视着黑汉子画星星——

　　原作每行七音节,重音数及位置毫无规则。因此译文中只顾
每行字数相等并与原作音节数接近,但不考虑诗行中的顿数。

　　最后还有一种诗律需要介绍一下,这就是主要存在于古英语
和中古英语诗歌中的头韵体,即诗行分两个半行,分别有两个读重
音的词以相同的辅音或元音开头(像汉语中的双声);各诗行中押
头韵之处不超过四个,不少于两个。通常的情况是:前半行中的两
个(或一个)重读音节与后半行的两个或前一个重读音节押头韵,
而这些格式在诗中可互相替换。

　　根据劳陇先生在上述《我》文中的传达,美国诗学家奈达说过:
"诗的格律……有意采用的头韵形式等等,都是不可翻译的语言现
象。"由此看来,头韵体的诗是肯定不能译的了。但英语中有句老
话说得好:Never is a long word。话不能说绝。手边正好有兰格伦
(1330? —1386?)长诗《农夫皮尔斯》的现代英语头韵体译文,请看
其头八行及拙译:

In a summer season, when soft was the sun
I Shaped me into shrouds as though I were a shepherd,
In habit like a hermit, unholy of works,
Went wide in this world, wonders to hear.
But on a May morning, on Malvern Hills,
There befell me a ferly, of fairy methought.
I was wearily wandered out, and went me to rest
Under a broad bank by a brook's side,

在煦和的夏日里,在暄暄阳光下

我穿上长袍，成了个牧羊人似的——
穿隐士的衣服，要做的却远非正事——
我徒步走天下，探听各种奇事。
是在五月一个上午，是在莫文山上，
我遇上了神奇的事，简直像神话。
我一路上走来，已感到劳累，
便走向溪边，去歇息在宽阔的岸上，

　　在我看来，这译诗已反映了原作格律，甚至可以说已译出了"头韵体"的格律特点。可见，检验译诗的唯一标准也应当是实践，而不是某位学者或名人的只言片语，因为他们的话同样做不到句句是真理。译诗问题是个非常复杂的问题，意见有分歧，做法上有不同都是正常现象。要解决问题，得拿出说理透彻的有说服力的观点，得拿出足以证明自己观点的译例。

　　相反，听到有人说什么早时胡适对"以顿代步"的英诗汉译作的评语是："这就像让西洋女人包小脚"，就觉得这是"胡适早就看出了这样做的弊病"，① 似乎这种说法为"民族化"译诗开辟了道路。其实，在译诗中首先不用文言并抛弃用我国传统诗形式束缚外国诗内容这种做法的，正是胡适。再看他译的那首"柔巴依"同用"以顿代步"等较高要求译出的相比较，就可看出，在这译诗问题上，他这句话能够有多少分量。

　　同样的情形还有。一位权威学者在其文章中谈及译诗，引用了美国诗人弗罗斯特（1874—1963）和德国诗人莫根斯泰恩（1871—1914）的两句刻薄话：前者说，诗是"在翻译中丧失掉的东西"；后者说，诗歌翻译"只分坏和次坏的两种"。这些说法不仅完全否定了译诗的可能，而且对译诗这种认真、艰辛而又必要的工作作了不必要的挖苦。然而这位学者似乎犹嫌不足，对后一种说法再加发挥，让"坏"和"次坏"再坏加一等，因为据他解释，莫氏此言"也就是说，不是更坏的，就是坏的"。接着他又断言："一个译本以诗而论，也许不失为好'诗'，但作为原诗的复制，它终不免是坏'译'。"真是要叫译诗者在"坏"的怪圈里走投无路。

　　讲这些话的人尽管都大有来头，但来头大未必能证明道理对。即使以弗氏和莫氏本人的诗作为翻译对象，也都能证明他们的话

---

① 丰华瞻《我怎样翻译诗歌》(见上海外语教育出版社《丰华瞻译诗集·附录》)。

是言过其实的夸大之词① ——至少对汉语译文来说是这样——
毕竟译诗和语言在不断发展和完善。

六

　　为避免篇幅过大,本文中都用短短的一节诗或一首诗作例子。
但通过这些例子,同样可清楚看到,属于高难领域的译诗经历了阶
段分明的进化过程。从 19 世纪末严复开始以传统诗形式译诗起,
这种译法独步天下近二十年,终于出现了以胡适为发端的白话自
由诗译法并风行译坛。过了十来年,便出现了朱湘和孙大雨,他们
分别从音节和音组(即顿)的角度出发,反映原作中音节数和音步
数,开始了由随意性很大的感性译诗到感性 - 理性译诗,由定性译
诗到在一定程度上可与原作格律"接轨"的定性 - 定量译诗的探索
(因为格律诗的语言是一种量化了的语言)。

　　发芽和成熟之间总有一个时间差。这两种探索大获成功之
时,似在半个世纪之后——显然这时间差大大超过了正常发展所
需要的。总之,在 1980 年前后,似乎一下子就出现了不少按上述
两种要求译出的成功的译诗集,同时也出现了用一种新的、综合了
这两者的要求译出的诗集,即按"兼顾诗行顿数与字数"要求译的
《柔巴依集》。

　　从上面一首柔巴依的八种译文,我们可以看到译诗在内容与
形式两方面朝原作的步步逼近。这种逼近证明了现代汉语具有极
大的潜力,能在忠实于原作内容的同时,还在很大程度上反映原作
的格律形式;而且,要反映原作形式,未必就有损于对原作内容的
忠实,两者是可以并存的。而译诗要求的提高,表明对这种潜力的
认识有了提高,于是用较高的要求来调动和挖掘它,同时也调动和
挖掘我们自身的潜力。

　　译诗的进化,实际上就是译诗要求的进化。这既可体现在某
个群体的译诗上,也可体现在一些个人的译诗经历上。我猜想,绝

① 请参阅《诗,未必是"在翻译中丧失掉的东西"——兼谈汉语在译诗中的潜力》
(《外国语》1995/2);《诗歌翻译"是否只分坏和次坏的两种"——兼谈汉字在译
诗中的潜力》(《现代外语》1997/1);或拙著《从柔巴依到坎特伯雷——英语诗
汉译研究》(湖北教育版,1999)。

大多数注意反映原作形式的译者,在译诗之初都并非如此。我本人就尝试过多种译法,最后才摸索到"兼顾诗行顿数与字数"的译诗要求,在实践中对它的可行性越来越有信心,终于按此要求译出长约两万行并含有多种诗体的英诗源头之作《坎特伯雷故事》,①并对以前的译诗按此种要求进行修改。

对旧译进行修改,使之符合某种能在一定程度上反映原作格律的做法,几乎是每一个有这种要求的译者必然采用过的,而且这样修改出来的译本也往往是比较成熟和成功的。例如杨德豫于五十年代末初版的《朗费罗诗选》中,诗"基本上都是译成了'半自由体',绝大多数译诗都未讲求顿数的整齐,韵式(脚韵安排)也只有半数左右的译诗是严格按照原诗的"。但到八十年代修订时,就把"以格律体译格律体"作为确定不移的原则,也即力求译诗格律反映原作格律。

由此可见,一个立志译诗的人最好尽早地研究一下原作的诗律,同时也研究一下各种译诗要求并选择较能反映原作格律形式的,这样既有利于让人们接受其译诗,也可减少日后修改时的工作量,免得积重难返。因为当人们发现汉语译诗有可能同时反映原作格律后,必然会提出这种要求,而且这必将成为译诗的一种趋势。毕竟,原作是内容与形式完美结合的精品,译诗也应当尽可能如此。

也许有人会对我说的这种趋势表示怀疑,因为眼下人们看到的译诗中大多还是采用自由诗或半自由诗译法的。对此,我认为数量不应成为判断的标准,问题在于质量,要看哪一种译诗有较大的持久性。另外,我们还可以从三方面来看这种趋势:

1) 任何一位经常修改旧译的译者也许都有体会,也即修改得最多的往往是那些原先不求反映原作形式的旧译,就是说,这种译文较不稳定,对它改动的幅度也往往较大。相反,能反映原作格律形式的译诗就较稳定,对它的修改往往是在现成的格律框架内作些"微调",除非在如何反映原作格律上有了新的要求。

2) 就我所见,译者的译诗要求发生变化时,这种变化多为"单向的",也即按我前面所述的译诗进化的方向变,而极少逆向的变,这说明对译诗反映原作的要求越来越高或越来越全面。

---

① 也许正因为这种译法"为今后用汉诗来翻译英语诗歌走出了一条新路",此书以最高得票数获第四届(1997—1998年)全国优秀外国文学图书一等奖。

3）要求译诗还反映原作格律的做法不仅存在于英诗汉译中。余振的早期译诗已注意到原作格律，经反复修改，他1980年初版的厚厚一本《莱蒙托夫诗选》已做到"兼顾诗行顿数与字数"。钱春绮在初译德语诗时用的是扣字数的译法，但到八十年代初，已改为"以顿代步"并注意控制译诗诗行字数。此外，兴万生从匈牙利文译出的《裴多菲诗选》（1990），李鸿影从波兰文译出的密茨凯维支的《潘·塔代乌士》（1994），都已注意反映原作形式并在诗行的"音步与字数"方面下了功夫。

当然译诗的进化还得力于一些别的因素，例如新诗的格律化探索和译诗的相对普及化。我们知道，译诗和新诗一直是息息相关的，长久以来大量的自由化译诗必然会造成很多读者和诗人的误解，以为外国诗是没有格律的，从而对诗创作带来影响，而创作出来的大量自由诗又似乎反过来使自由化译诗有更大的市场。

至于说"普及"，从上面那些例子就可看出，早期的重要译诗者大多是多方面发展的文化界顶尖人物，但后来越来越"普及"了，于是译诗也就相对地专业化和学术化起来，成为颇具独立性的领域。反过来，译诗的专业化和学术化程度越高，对译诗的进化也就越有利。

当然，译诗的进化也是有一定限度的，因为原作是固定不变的。当译诗进化到一定阶段，进化到已能在较高程度上反映原作格律，例如上面以相应的形式译"头韵体"原作或以"兼顾诗行顿数与字数"的要求译常规意义上的音步诗，这时，对前者来说，已把事情做到了头，在译诗要求上已没有继续进化的余地。而对后者来说，尽管事情还没有做到头，但看来也只能"适可而止"了。因为如果还要继续进化的话，那就是要在译文中反映原作的音步是什么格的问题了。英语诗中的音步有抑扬格、抑抑扬格、扬抑格、扬抑抑格、抑扬抑格等。如何在汉语译诗中区分以这些不同格音步建行的诗句，或者是否可能作这样的区分，或者做到这种区分的可能有多大……这些问题我还没作过研究，无法回答。

就我来说，目前只能满足于"兼顾诗行顿数与字数"的要求，幸好，英语格律诗中绝大多数是以抑扬格音步建行的。

*

1996年2月下旬的《文汇读书周报》"经理荐书"上，上海外文图书公司两位老总推荐的十本书中,包含本书及其姐妹篇《英国抒情诗 100 首》。这当然使我很高兴,因为我觉得在译诗中,失真的可能性实在太大了:人们有时为了追求"诗意"而在译文里添油加酱,有时则根据自己的需要而对原作中的内容任意删削,认为这是"正确地理解'忠实'的意义";对原作的格律形式似乎就更随便了,有时把原作的内容硬塞进某种与原作格律无关的固定模式,有时则不予理会,把诗歌形式中包含的各种信息一扔了之。所以,我觉得比较理想的译诗应当在内容与形式上经得起与原作对照,而译诗比较理想的出版形式也应当是有两种文字对照的。

但是诗歌格律是一种专门知识,广大的读者不大可能在读英语诗原作前让自己具备这种知识。因此即使我们面前放着原作,我们仍可能不知道这是一首格律诗,更不知道这是一首什么格律的诗。这样说来,译诗集或对照译诗集中最好先能介绍一些有关外国诗歌格律的常识,然后向读者交代一下译文中是如何处理原作格律的。但就我看到的大量对照本而言,绝大部分都没有这种内容。

这情形并不奇怪。以上面提到的我那本《英国抒情诗 100 首》而言,它初版于 1986 年,交稿则在 1982 年,其中很多的诗早在文革初就已译出,而当时我还没见过专谈英诗格律的书籍。因此,尽管在实践的过程中,我已隐约感到译诗有必要在忠实于原作内容的同时,也尽可能反映其形式,但在做法上还只是在朝这个方向努力,还没有形成一种非常明确的译诗标准。于是在这本译诗集里,有我一些早期译诗的遗迹,这主要表现在有少量译诗走的是"民族化"与"自由化"一路,有不少译诗走的是只顾诗行字数的一路。既然自己对英诗格律也不甚了了,对应该如何译还在摸索之中,那当然还是"不谈为妙"。

但本书的情况已略有不同,它初版于 1994 年,内容几乎全部是新译,而这时我对英语诗的格律已略有所知,对应当如何译诗也已有了较明确的要求。只是考虑到本书是上一本书的姐妹篇,而上一本中没有"前言",所以本书初版时只是在"后记"中极简单地谈了下这两方面的情况。

根据我这种译诗要求,理想的译诗不仅应当在韵式和诗行的顿数上与原作的一致,还应当让诗行的音节数(字数)与原作的相近并有对应关系。这可说是迄今为止最严格的要求,而且就我所见,也仅我一人在按我建立的这种要求翻译英美诗歌。我写了很多论文,从各方面论证了这种要求的合理性、必要性和可取性,也谈到其可行性——事实上它不像想象中那么难,那么会影响意思的表达。

论文中的例子毕竟很少,远不如用整个一本书作例子。我想,只要随便看看本书中的格律诗译文,看看 172、218、220、242、286、294 等页上的诗及其译文,就会对上述"四性"有一深刻印象。当然,对这两个姐妹篇,我也趁再版重印之机补上了内容充实的论文作为前言。

本书的前言是我迄今为止写得最长的,因为它是对一百多年来英语诗汉译的回顾,可说是一篇发展史。现在新世纪正迎面而来,我希望,本书这次面世时,它所带的这篇拙文① 能成为对新世纪英语诗汉译事业的小小奉献。我也相信,在一个更重视译诗质量的环境里,本文所提倡的译诗要求将会结出更丰硕的果实。

最后需要说明的是,这次重印中已对十六首诗的译文作了修改,其中,除了 191 与 295 页上的两诗改动较多外,都只是个别词语的修改。改动的幅度这么小,恐怕在很大程度上就因为译这些诗时已有了较高、较明确的要求。

黄杲炘

2000 年秋

---

①　本文中的一部分曾发表在 2000 年 9 月 30 日的《文汇读书周报》上。

CONTENTS

目 录

---

*　为便于识别，目录中的女诗人译名用全名，男诗人则单用姓氏。

美国抒情诗 100 首

（英汉对照）

THE AUTHOR TO HER BOOK

Thou ill-formed offspring of my feeble brain, [1]

Who after birth didst by my side remain, [2]

Till snatched from thence by friends, less wise than true, [3]

Who thee abroad exposed to public view, [4]

Made thee in rags, halting to th' press to trudge, [5]

Where errors were not lessened (all may judge).

At thy return my blushing was not small,

My rambling brat (in print) should mother call, [6]

I cast thee by as one unfit for light, [7]

Thy visage was so irksome in my sight; [8]

Yet being mine own, at length affection would [9]

Thy blemishes amend, if so I could;

---

[1] Thou：[古、诗]＝You，这里是呼语；本行的其余部分是它的同位语，随后五行是定语从句。

[2] didst by my side remain＝didst remain by my side；didst remain＝remained；-st：[古、诗]接动词后，构成陈述语气第二人称单数。

[3] Till snatched＝Till thou wast [you were] snatched. less wise than true：真诚有余，聪明不足。

[4] Who thee abroad＝Who, taking thee [you 的单数宾格] abroad；Who 的谓语动词是下行的 Made。

[5] halting：此词有"跛行"、"踌躇"两义，这里指"跛行"，见后面作者犹图 make thee even feet（使不跛足）和更后面的 run'st more hobbling（跑得更加一瘸一拐）。

作者致自己的诗集

我无力的头脑产下幼稚的你；

出生后你本来同我待在一起，

直到被忠实的糊涂朋友拿掉，

把褴褛的你带了出去给人瞧，

让你瘸着腿费劲踏进印刷所：

人人看得出，那儿没帮你改错。

见你回来，我羞得涨红了面庞，

就怕白纸黑字的浑小鬼叫娘。

我把你丢开，感到你不该出生，

因为见你那模样我不免恼恨；

可既是我骨肉，只要我能做到，

我的爱总想使你的瑕疵减少：

---

⑥ My rambling brat：前面省略连词 For，说明上行 my blushing was not small 的缘故。should mother call＝should call me mother.

⑦ unfit for light：不宜出世，不宜出版；按习语 see the light 的意思就是"出世"或"出版"。

⑧ Thy：[Your，单数所有格]，本句中用 so，说明上行 I cast thee by 的原因，起连词作用。

⑨ being mine own ＝being my own；句中主语 affection 不是这个分词短语的逻辑上的主语，因而这个分词称为"垂悬分词"(dangling participle)；诗中常见这种不规范的语法现象。

I washed thy face, but more defects I saw,

And rubbing off a spot still made a flaw.

I stretched thy joints to make thee even feet,[10]

Yet still thou run'st more hobbling than is meet;[11]

In better dress to trim thee was my mind,

But nought save homespun cloth i' th' house I find.[12]

In this array 'mongst vulgars may'st thou roam.[13]

In critic's hands beware thou dost not come,

And take thy way where yet thou art not known;

If for thy father asked, say thou hadst none;[14]

And for thy mother, she alas is poor,[15]

Which caused her thus to send thee out of door.[16]

---

[10] to make thee even feet：这里的 even feet（两足齐而不跛）可视为一个复合词,犹如因较常使用而已合并成一个单词的 barefoot, clubfoot 等。feet 还指诗中的音步,故这里是一语双关。

[11] run'st more hobbling than is meet：run'st=runnest,这里为格律需要而省略一个音节；hobbling(跛行)可视为表语,也可视为状语；than is meet 中的 than 在这里起 is 的主语的作用,是一个特殊的习惯用法；meet,形容词,"合适"之意。

[12] nought save=nothing but=only；这里的 save 和 but 都=except。i' th'=in the,为格律需要而省略一个音节,读作[ið]。本诗的格律是流行于 17、18 世纪的"英雄偶句体",其特点是：每行为构成五音步的十个音节,两行押一韵。

我替你洗脸，却看见更多缺点；

擦去了污渍，还是留下个缺陷。

我拉你关节，要你双脚一样长，

可是一跑动，你跛得更不像样；

我想用漂亮衣裳把你打扮好，

但家里只能找到粗糙的衣料。

穿这衣服去平民间流浪无妨，

可要留神别落进评论家手掌。

你去的地方要没人同你相熟，

要是谁问起你父亲，就说没有；

问起你母亲，就说她呀苦得很，

这就使得她送你这模样出门。

---

⑬　'mongst = amongst = among. vulgars = common people. may'st = mayest.

⑭　If for thy father asked = If thou art [you are] asked for your father.

⑮　本行承上行，= And if thou art asked for thy mother, say she alas is poor. alas, 插入的惊叹词, 表示悲伤、遗憾。

⑯　Which: 指 she is poor 境况。

UPON THE SWEEPING FLOOD

Oh! that I'd had a tear to've quenched that flame①

  Which did dissolve the heavens above

  Into those liquid drops that came

    To drown our carnal love.

Our cheeks were dry and eyes refused to weep.

Tears bursting out ran down the sky's dark cheek.

Were th'heavens sick? Must we their doctors be

  And physic them with pills, our sin?②

  To make them purge and vomit, see,

    And excrements out fling?③

We've grieved them by such physic that they shed④

Their excrements upon our lofty heads.⑤

---

① Oh! that ...：也可单用 That... =How I wish that...。to've [təv]=to have，为格
律需要，缩略一个音节。下节第 1 行的 th'heavens 同。

② physic：给……服药，尤指给服泻药。our sin 是 pills 的同位语，所谓〈致泻〉的丸药就
是我们的罪孽，尤其妙在 pill 兼有"令人厌恶的东西"之意。

有感于滔滔雨势

啊,但愿我先前有许许多多泪,
　　多得能浇灭云霄中的火——
　　它把天空熔成滴滴的水,
　　　　来将肉体的爱淹没。
可眼睛不肯哭,我们的脸很干。
天迸出了泪,淌下它暗淡的脸。

难道天病了? 我们得做它大夫——
　　我们的罪孽给它做泻药?
　　瞧,不是要使它下泻上吐,
　　　　把该排泄的全出掉?
我们的泻药已经使天空悲伤,
使它排泄在我们高傲的头上。

---

③　excrements out fling＝fling out excrements.

④　physic:作"药品、泻药"解,是口语。

⑤　本诗中,每节都是六行,各行的音步分别为 5,4,4,3,5,5,为了让这种情况使读者一目了然,诗人对诗的左端作了齐头或缩进的处理(indentation)。

THE VOLUNTEER'S MARCH
Dulce est pro patria mori.

Ye,whom Washington has led,[①]
Ye,who in his footsteps tread,
Ye,who death nor danger dread,[②]
Haste to glorious victory.

Now's the day and now's the hour;
See the British navy lour,[③]
See approach proud George's power,[④]
England! chains and slavery.

Who would be a traitor knave?
Who would fill a coward's grave?
Who so base to be a slave?[⑤]
Traitor, coward, turn and flee.[⑥]

Meet the tyrants, one and all;[⑦]
Freemen stand, or freemen fall—[⑧]
At Columbia's patriot call,[⑨]
At her mandate, march away!

---

① Ye：[古、诗]＝You(主格). 上面的拉丁文副题出自罗马诗人贺拉斯。
② death nor danger dread＝dread neither death nor danger.
③ lour[lauə]：也作 lower，威胁，本义为"(天)阴下来"，"(风雪等)似将到来"。
④ 本行＝See proud George's power approach；George 指英王乔治三世。
⑤ 本行承上行＝Who would be so base as to be a slave?

义勇军进行曲
为国而死就死得美

你们,曾是华盛顿的部下,
你们,踩着他足迹跟随他,
你们,死亡和险阻都不怕,
　　赶快去夺取光辉的胜利。

今天的此刻要决定命运;
瞧不列颠舰队正在逼近,
瞧骄横的乔治正在进军——
　　英格兰就是锁链和奴役!

谁愿做一个卖国的贼子?
谁愿埋葬在懦夫的墓里?
谁下贱得宁愿做个奴隶?
　　卖国贼和懦夫滚离此地!

要万众一心去迎战暴君;
为自由去战斗或者献身,
听得祖国母亲的呼召声,
　　听得她命令便奋勇向前。

---

⑥　turn and flee:是祈使语气。

⑦　one and all:人人全都,是习语。

⑧　本行＝Stand (as) freemen or fall(as) freemen,句型同 He died a hero(他死为英
雄);or ＝or else,否则。

⑨　Columbia:[诗]美洲或美国的女性拟人化称呼。

Former times have seen them yield,[⑩]
Seen them drove from every field,[⑪]
Routed, ruin'd and repell'd—[⑫]
　Seize the spirit of those times!

By oppression's woes and pains—[⑬]
By our sons in servile chains
We will bleed from all our veins
　But they shall be—shall be free.

O'er the standard of their power
Bid Columbia's eagle tower,[⑭]
Give them hail in such a shower
　As shall blast them—horse and man![⑮]

Lay the proud invaders low,
Tyrants fall in every foe;
Liberty's in every blow,
　Forward! Let us do or die.

---

⑩　Former times：从前。

⑪　drove＝driven.

⑫　Routed，ruin'd and repell'd：三个有 r 头韵的近义词连用，有声有色地活现敌军兵败
　　如山倒。

从前他们也曾经打败仗，
被杀得逃离一处处战场，
只剩些溃散的残兵败将——
　　你们要继承当时那精神！

凭受压迫者的苦难起誓，
凭将受奴役的子孙起誓，
我们愿流尽血管里的血，
　　但他们必须，必须获自由。

让美利坚之鹰高高翱翔，
翱翔在他们的军旗之上；
为把他们杀得马翻人仰，
　　要让子弹密集得像暴雨！

杀败骄傲入侵者的三军，
死一个敌人，少一分暴政；
打击多一次，自由增一分，
　　前进，干不成就宁可阵亡！

---

⑬　By：以……起誓，如常见的 By God。

⑭　这两行＝Bid Columbia's eagle tower over the standard of their power；eagle，指美
军的鹰旗；tower over，凌驾于……之上；standard，军旗。

⑮　horse and man：连人带马，作状语。比较习语 horse and foot，骑兵和步兵。

THE POET

Thou, who wouldst wear the name

    Of poet mid thy brethren of mankind, ①

And clothe in words of flame

    Thoughts that shall live within the general mind!

Deem not the framing of a deathless lay

The pastime of a drowsy summer day.

But gather all thy powers,

    And wreak them on the verse that thou dost weave.

And in thy lonely hours,

    At silent morning or at wakeful eve,

While the warm current tingles through thy veins,

Set forth the burning words in fluent strains.

No smooth array of phrase, ②

    Artfully sought and ordered though it be,

Which the cold rhymer lays

    Upon his page with languid industry,

Can wake the listless pulse to livelier speed,

Or fill with sudden tears the eyes that read .

---

① mid: [诗] = amid.

诗　人

在普天下的兄弟间，

　　你愿让自己享有诗人的名望，

想要用火样的语言

　　抒发将活在众人心头的思想！

别以为创作一首不朽的小诗

只是为打发一个懒散的夏日。

这要求你集中精力，

　　把力量全用于编织你的诗篇，

要求你在独处之时，

　　无论在静静早晨或不眠夜晚，

当你周身的血管里热血涌流，

你张口把炽热流畅的诗唱出。

冷冰冰的打油诗人

　　有气无力地凭一点技巧写诗；

这些诗虽文通字顺，

　　尽管被精心装点得整齐美丽，

却难使无精打采的脉搏加快，

难使读者的泪在眼中涌起来。

---

② array of phrase：词藻的装饰。这个名词词组的谓语动词是三行后的 Can wake。

The secret wouldst thou know[3]

　To touch the heart or fire the blood at will?[4]

Let thine own eyes o'erflow;

　Let thy lips quiver with the passionate thrill;

Seize the great thought, ere its power be past,

And bind, in words, the fleet emotion fast.[5]

Then, should thy verse appear

　Halting and harsh, and all unaptly wrought,

Touch the crude line with fear,[6]

　Save in the moment of impassioned thought;[7]

Then summon back the original glow, and mend

The strain with rapture that with fire was penned.[8]

Yet let no empty gust

　Of passion find an utterance in thy lay,

A blast that whirls the dust[9]

　Along the howling street and dies away;

But feelings of calm power and mighty sweep,[10]

Like currents journeying through the windless deep.[11]

---

③　本行＝Thou would know the secret；下行的不定式短语修饰 The secret。

④　at will：任意地，是习语，修饰 touch 和 fire。

⑤　本行＝And bind the fleet emotion fast in words；fast，牢固的，可靠的，这里作宾语
　　补足语。

⑥　with fear：战战兢兢地。

⑦　Save＝Except。

想知道要触动人心，
　　要读者的血沸腾起来的秘诀？
先让泪充满你眼睛，
　　先让你的嘴唇因激情而颤栗，
在伟大的思想逝去前抓住它，
并把倏忽的感情用文字写下。

倘这时你的诗看来
　　滞涩而粗糙，写得也很不得体，
那就得小心地修改，
　　不过情绪激动的时候要回避；
尔后唤回你当初欣喜的热情，
把你激情似火时写的诗修订。

但是在你写的诗中，
　　别让无聊的闲情有容身之地，
这是挟灰尘的阵风，
　　呼啸着掠过街道便渐渐平息；
诗情要沉静而有宏伟的力量，
就像是海流涌过无风的大洋。

---

⑧　mend /The strain with rapture that with fire was penned；with rapture 修饰 mend，
　　that with fire was penned (＝that was penned with fire) 修饰 The strain。
⑨　A blast：与前面的 empty gust/Of passion 同位。
⑩　本行中的 feelings 与 gust 并列。全行＝But let feelings of calm power and mighty
　　sweep find an utterance in thy lay.
⑪　deep：[诗] 海。

Seek'st thou, in living lays,

    To limn the beauty of the earth and sky?

Before thine inner gaze

    Let all that beauty in clear vision lie;

Look on it with exceeding love, and write

The words inspired by wonder and delight.

Of tempests wouldst thou sing,[12]

    Or tell of battles—make thyself a part

Of the great tumult; cling[13]

    To the tossed wreck with terror in thy heart;

Scale, with the assaulting host, the ramparts' height,[14]

And strike and struggle in the thickest fight.

So shalt thou frame a lay[15]

    That haply may endure from age to age,[16]

And they who read shall say:

    "What witchery hangs upon this poet's page!

What art is his the written spells to find

That sway from mood to mood the willing mind!"

---

[12] 本行＝Wouldst thou (would you)sing of tempests,虚拟语气,＝If you would sing of tempests.

[13] tumult：这里指狂风暴雨和战争。

[14] 本行＝Scale the ramparts' height(together)with the assaulting host; scale,攀登,用云梯进攻; host,[古] 军队; height,顶点。

在生气勃勃的诗内

　　你想把天上和人间的美描画？
那先让所有那些美
　　清晰显现在你的心灵之前吧；
然后怀着挚爱把那图景细觑，
写下由惊异、喜悦激出的词句。

你要把暴风雨歌颂，
　　要描述战争？那你就得让自己
处身于那祸乱之中；
　　紧抱着颠簸的船板，满心惊悸，
或随进攻的大军往城墙上爬，
在战斗最为激烈的地方拼杀。

你这样写成的诗歌
　　有可能把一个一个时代经历，
让读你诗的人们说：
　　"这位诗人的作品多么有魅力！
他所掌握的诗艺简直是符咒，
能够把心悦诚服的读者左右！"

---

⑮　So=Thus.

⑯　That=Which，代替上行末的 lay；这里的 That 与上行的 So 并无相互呼应的搭配关系。

I BROKE THE SPELL THAT HELD ME LONG[①]

I broke the spell that held me long,
The dear, dear witchery of song.[②]
I said, the poet's idle lore
Shall waste my prime of years no more,
For Poetry, though heavenly born,
Consorts with poverty and scorn.

I broke the spell—nor deemed its power
Could fetter me another hour.
Ah, thoughtless! how could I forget
Its causes were around me yet?[③]
For whereso'er I looked, the while,[④]
Was Nature's everlasting smile.

Still came and lingered on my sight[⑤]
Of flowers and streams the bloom and light,
And glory of the stars and sun;—
And these and poetry are one.
They, ere the world had held me long,
Recalled me to the love of song.

---

① 本诗原文用第 1 行为标题；据此，译文也用第一行译诗作标题。
② witchery of song 是上行 spell 的同位语。
③ Its causes＝The causes of the spell.

诗歌的魔力久久控制我

诗歌的魔力久久控制我，
可我挣脱它迷人的诱惑；
我说过，诗人的徒然劝导
再不能把我的青春消耗，
因为虽然说诗歌最神圣，
招来的却是轻视和穷困。

我挣脱它诱惑，不再认为
它还有力量抓住我一会。
真是粗心！我怎能忘记
我周围依然是诗的天地？
因为我随时朝哪里一看，
总见一直在笑的大自然。

盛开的花朵、闪闪的溪流，
辉煌的太阳、璀璨的星斗，
仍出现、逗留在我眼睑上，
而这些同诗本就是一样。
没等我在俗世之中久待，
它们又唤我去把诗歌爱。

---

④ the while：与此同时。

⑤ came and lingered：这两个谓语动词的主语是后面的 the bloom and light 和更后面的 glory of the stars and sun。

GEORGE MOSES HORTON, MYSELF

I feel myself in need
    Of the inspiring strains of ancient lore,
My heart to lift, my empty mind to feed,[1]
    And all the world explore.[2]

I know that I am old
    And never can recover what is past,
But for the future may some light unfold[3]
    And soar from ages blast.[4]

I feel resolved to try,
    My wish to prove, my calling to pursue,
Or mount up from the earth into the sky,
    To show what Heaven can do.

My genius from a boy,
    Has fluttered like a bird within my heart;
But could not thus confined her powers employ,[5]
    Impatient to depart.

She like a restless bird,
    Would spread her wings, her power to be unfurl'd[6]
And let her songs be loudly heard,
    And dart from world to world.

---

① 本行＝To lift my heart, to feed my empty mind.

② 本行＝And to explore all the world.

③ 本行＝But may unfold some light for the future.

我，乔治·摩西·霍顿

我感到，自己需要
　　　古传说里那种激励振奋的诗，
来鼓雄心，来充实空虚的头脑——
　　　去探索整个人世。

我知道我已年迈，
　　　已永远不能挽回消逝的过去；
但是，将来也许还能展现光彩，
　　　远离长期的打击。

我决心进行尝试，
　　　检验我的愿望，施展我的抱负；
要不就升天，就离开这个尘世——
　　　显示老天的身手。

我从小有的天赋
　　　在我的心中像鸟儿拍着翅膀；
但这样给关着，她有劲使不出，
　　　却又急着要翱翔。

她会像焦躁的鸟
　　　张开双翼，展示出自己的力量，
唱出嘹亮的歌声让世人听到，
　　　并猛地直冲天上。

---

④　本行＝And blast may soar from ages. from ages＝from the past.

⑤　本行＝But (being) thus confined, could not employ her powers.

⑥　her power to be unfurl'd＝so that her power would be unfurled.

CONCORD HYMN[①]

Sung at the completion of the Battle Monument, July 4, 1837

By the rude bridge that arched the flood,[②]
　Their flag to April's breeze unfurled,[③]
Here once the embattled farmers stood
　And fired the shot heard round the world.

The foe long since in silence slept,[④]
　Alike the conqueror silent sleeps;[⑤]
And Time the ruined bridge has swept
　Down the dark stream which seaward creeps.

On this green bank, by this soft stream,
　We set today a votive stone;
That memory may their deed redeem,[⑥]
　When, like our sires, our sons are gone.[⑦]

Spirit, that made those heroes dare[⑧]
　To die, and leave their children free,
Bid Time and Nature gently spare
　The shaft we raise to them and thee.[⑨]

---

① Concord：美国马萨诸塞州东部城市，为独立战争时（1775 年）战场，后因爱默生、霍桑等文人居住而更闻名。

② flood：[诗] 河。

③ 本行＝Their flag (being) unfurled to April's breeze，是个独立结构，表示伴随情况。

④ The foe：敌军的总称。long since：（从上节描述的战争时起）长久以来，是习语。

康 科 德 赞 歌

为康科德之战纪念碑落成而咏
1936 年 7 月 4 日

在当年横跨河水的陋桥近旁，
　　　他们的旗帜曾迎着春风飘展；
这是庄稼汉投入战斗的地方，
　　　他们的枪声曾被全世界听见。

敌人无声无息地早躺在地下，
　　　胜利者也安安静静正在沉睡；
倒塌的断桥经不住时光冲刷，
　　　落进蜿蜒入海的黑黝黝河水。

在这道缓缓小河的青青岸上，
　　　今天我们立一座石碑表心愿：
尽管祖祖孙孙一代代地消亡，
　　　让英雄们的业绩仍被人怀念。

啊，曾激励英雄们敢于牺牲，
　　　勇于为子孙争取自由的精神！
请吩咐时光和风雷雨雪留情——
　　　让纪念他们和你的石碑永存。

---

⑤　silent＝silently.

⑥　That＝So that.

⑦　sires：男性祖先。

⑧　Spirit：这里是呼语。

⑨　shaft：本义为"杆"，这里指建立的纪念碑。

FABLE

The mountain and the squirrel
Had a quarrel,
And the former called the latter "Little Prig";[①]
Bun replied,[②]
"You are doubtless very big;
But all sorts of things and weather
Must be taken in together,
To make up a year
And a sphere.
And I think it no disgrace
To occupy my place.
If I'm not so large as you,
You are not so small as I,
And not half so spry,
I'll not deny you make
A very pretty squirrel track;
Talents differ; all is well and wisely put;
If I cannot carry forests on my back,
Neither can you crack a nut. "

---

① Prig：一本正经或自命不凡的人，有贬义。

寓　言

大山和松鼠曾经吵过，
前者把后者叫做
"自鸣得意的小东西"。
松鼠回答：
"你当然很大；
但要把所有的东西
和时节全合在一起，
这才能构成岁月
和构成一个世界。
所以我占这么个位置，
我认为决没什么可耻。
倘要说我没有你大，
那么你也不如我小，
而且远不如我灵巧。
我并不否认你为松鼠
提供了非常漂亮的路径；
但各有所长；万物各得其所；
要说我背脊上带不了森林，
那你也没本事咬开个坚果。"

---

② Bun：[口] 松鼠。

MUSIC

Let me go where'er I will,
I hear a sky-born music still:[①]
It sounds from all things old,
It sounds from all things young,
From all that's fair, from all that's foul,
Peals out a cheerful song.

It is not only in the rose,
It is not only in the bird,
Not only where the rainbow glows,
Nor in the song of woman heard,[②]
But in the darkest, meanest things
There alway, alway something sings.[③]

'T is not in the high stars alone,
Nor in the cup of budding flowers,
Nor in the redbreast's mellow tone,
Nor in the bow that smiles in showers,[④]
But in the mud and scum of things
There alway, alway something sings.

---

① sky-born:[诗] 在天界产生的。still:[古] always.
② 本句＝Nor in the song heard of woman. of＝from.

音 乐

任我去我想去的一切地方，
我常听见出自空中的音乐：
一切古老的东西发这音响，
它也来自一切年轻的东西；
从一切正直和一切邪恶的，
响亮地送出一支欢乐的歌。

这音乐不单单存在于玫瑰，
这音乐不单单存在于飞鸟，
它不单把鲜艳的彩虹追随，
不单在女子的歌中被听到；
在最最阴暗卑贱的事物中，
也总有些东西会发出歌声。

它不单存在于高空的星星，
不单同新吐的花苞在一起，
不单在知更鸟甜润的歌中
或者笑看着彩虹的阵雨里；
就在万物的垃圾和渣滓中，
也总有些东西会发出歌声。

---

③ 第二节整节是一句，其基本结构是 It is not only in..., nor (only) in...,but(also)
in...(that) there alway, alway something sings；alway,[古、诗]=always.

④ bow＝rainbow.

THE DAY IS DONE[①]

The day is done, and the darkness
　　Falls from the wings of night,
As a feather is wafted downward
　　From an eagle in his flight.

I see the lights of the village
　　Gleam through the rain and the mist,
And a feeling of sadness comes o'er me.
　　That my soul cannot resist:

A feeling of sadness and longing,
　　That is not akin to pain,
And resembles sorrow only
　　As the mist resembles the rain.

Come, read to me some poem,
　　Some simple and heartfelt lay,
That shall soothe this restless feeling,
　　And banish the thoughts of day.

Not from the grand old masters,
　　Not from the bards sublime,[②]
Whose distant footsteps echo
　　Through the corridors of time.

---

① Done:过去分词形成的形容词,作"完毕"解。参见英国现代诗人 Sassoon 著名小诗
Everyone Sang 末行 The singing will never be done,不是"永不歌唱",而是"歌唱永
不休止"之意。

白 天 已 结 束

白天已结束，从夜的翅膀
　　渐渐地落下了黑暗，
就像是从翱翔的鹰身上
　　飘下了它羽毛一片。

透过雨和雾，我隐隐看见
　　村子里闪烁的灯光，
而一种惆怅就向我袭来。
　　对于它我无法抵挡：

这是种惆怅也是种渴望，
　　和痛苦却并不一样，
只是和悲哀有几分相似，
　　就如同雾和雨相像。

给我来念念纯朴的诗吧，
　　念一点真挚的小曲；
让它抚慰这烦闷的感情，
　　驱除掉白天的思虑。

不用找古代杰出的大师，
　　不用找高雅的诗豪，
他们在时光的长廊里面
　　脚步声已经太迢遥。

---

② bards sublime＝sublime bards；sublime，庄严的，崇高的，诗中也作"傲慢的"解；
bards，古代的行吟诗人，史诗作者。

For, like strains of martial music,
 Their mighty thoughts suggest
Life's endless toil and endeavor;
 And tonight I long for rest.

Read from some humbler poet,[3]
 Whose songs gushed from his heart,
As showers from the clouds of summer,
 Or tears from the eyelids start;[4]

Who, through long days of labor,
 And nights devoid of ease,[5]
Still heard in his soul the music
 Of wonderful melodies.

Such songs have power to quiet
 The restless pulse of care,
And come like the benediction
 That follows after prayer.

Then read from the treasured volume
 The poem of thy choice,
And lend to the rhyme of the poet[6]
 The beauty of thy voice.

And the night shall be filled with music,
 And the cares, that infest the day,
Shall fold their tents, like the Arabs,
 And as silently steal away.[7]

---

③　humbler poet：humble，谦虚的，也作"地位低下"解。

④　这两行＝As showers start from the clouds of summer，or tears start from the eyelids.

因为他们那伟大的思想
　　有如是一支军乐曲,
暗示了人生无尽的辛劳,
　　而今晚我渴求安歇。

请念些通俗诗人的作品,
　　他的歌涌自他的心,
像骤雨出自夏日的云朵,
　　像泪水涌出了眼睛;

这诗人久经白天的操劳,
　　又缺少安恬的夜晚,
但是灵魂中的奇妙曲调
　　他依然还是能听见。

对于一阵阵不安的烦恼,
　　这种歌有力量平息;
就像随祈祷而来的祝福,
　　这种歌来给人慰藉。

所以从你珍爱的诗集中
　　请挑一首念给我听,
让诗人写下的抑扬韵律
　　添上你美好的嗓音。

这时候夜就充满了乐声,
　　而骚扰白天的烦恼
会像阿拉伯人收起帐篷,
　　不出声地悄悄走掉。

---

⑤　devoid of:缺乏……的;devoid,形容词,常作表语。

⑥　lend:把……给予;它的宾语是 The beauty of thy voice。

⑦　本行＝And steal away as silently as the Arabs.

THE SOUND OF THE SEA①

The sea awoke at midnight from its sleep,

    And round the pebbly beaches far and wide

    I heard the first wave of the rising tide②

Rush onward with uninterrupted sweep;

A voice out of the silence of the deep,

    A sound mysteriously multiplied

    As of a cataract from the mountain's side,

Or roar of winds upon a wooded steep.

So comes to us at times, from the unknown③

    And inaccessible solitudes of being,④

      The rushing of the sea-tides of the soul;

And inspirations, that we deem our own,

    Are some divine foreshadowing and foreseeing

    Of things beyond our reason or control.

---

① 这是一首十四行诗,其韵脚排列是意大利式的 abba abba cde cde。从本诗也可看出,
诗行的排列方式也可反映全诗的韵式(本诗中所有的诗行都是五音步的)。

② heard the first wave of the rising tide:后面 A voice,A sound,roar of winds 都与 the
first wave 并列,也可说都是同位语。

海 之 声

夜半时分大海从睡梦中苏醒，

　　我在处处都是卵石的海滩上

　　听见潮水涨时的第一排大浪

奔腾着向前涌来，一刻也不停；

这是无声的大海发出的噪音，

　　这种声音被玄妙地放大加强，

　　有如山坡上泻下的飞瀑一样，

像呼啸的风吹着陡处的山林。

同样，灵魂中潮汐的奔腾波澜

　　有时从难以捉摸的身心清寂，

　　　　从不知什么地方向我们涌来；

而我们视为纯属我们的灵感

　　是对某些事神妙的预兆、预示——

　　　　这些事却在我们理解、控制外。

---

③　comes：主语是后面的名词词组 the rushing of the sea-tides of the soul。

④　being：（人的）存在。

THE RAINY DAY

The day is cold, and dark, and dreary;

It rains, and the wind is never weary;

The vine still clings to the mouldering wall,

But at every gust the dead leaves fall,

    And the day is dark and dreary.

My life is cold, and dark, and dreary;

It rains, and the wind is never weary;

My thoughts still cling to the mouldering Past,

But the hopes of youth fall thick in the blast,[1]

    And the days are dark and dreary.

Be still, sad heart! and cease repining;

Behind the clouds is the sun still shining;[2]

Thy fate is the common fate of all,

Into each life some rain must fall,

    Some days must be dark and dreary.

---

① thick:在这里可视为表语,也可视为状语。

下　雨　的　日　子

这个日子又冷又闷又阴暗，
雨下个不停，风又不知疲倦；
藤蔓依然攀附着旧墙破壁，
但一阵风来，总有枯叶落地，
　　这个日子又闷又阴暗。

我的生活又冷又闷又阴暗，
雨下个不停，风又不知疲倦；
思绪仍然依附着往事旧梦，
青春的希望被风吹落泥尘，
　　这些日子又闷又阴暗。

安静吧忧伤的心，别再烦恼！
乌云后面总是有阳光照耀；
你的命运本和大家的相同：
风雨难免落到各人生活中，
　　有时难免又闷又阴暗。

---

② 本句＝The sun is still shining behind the clouds. still 有"始终"之意，请参考英谚
Every cloud has a silver lining，意谓黑暗中总有一线光明。

BARBARA FRIETCHIE[1]

Up from the meadows rich with corn,
Clear in the cool September morn,[2]

The clustered spires of Frederick stand[3]
Green-walled by the hills of Maryland.

Round about them orchards sweep,[4]
Apple and peach tree fruited deep,[5]

Fair as the garden of the Lord[6]
To the eyes of the famished rebel horde,[7]

On that pleasant morn of the early fall
When Lee marched over the mountain-wall;[8]

Over the mountains winding down,[9]
Horse and foot, into Frederick town.[10]

Forty flags with their silver stars,
Forty flags with their crimson bars,[11]

Flapped in the morning wind: then sun
Of noon looked down, and saw not one.[12]

① Barbara Frietchie：美国内战中一平凡而真实的人物,事迹见本诗。
② 第 1 节两行修饰下一节中的 stand,诗歌中句子跨节是常有的；rich with corn 是后置定语短语,修饰 meadows；corn 在英国统指谷类,在美国指玉米。
③ Frederick：美国马里兰州的工业城市。
④ 本行＝Orchards sweep round about them；sweep,连绵,形成一片；them, 指 hill.
⑤ fruited deep ：果实累累；deep＝abundantly.
⑥ the garden of the Lord：伊甸园,见《圣经·旧约·以西结书》第 28 章第 13 节"你曾在伊甸上帝的园中"。

芭芭拉·弗里奇

那草原上玉米长得茂盛，
那是个凉爽的五月之晨，

弗市的尖塔一簇簇耸立，
马里兰的山像一堵绿壁。

多少果园绵延在那四周，
园中的桃子苹果正成熟；

在饿得发慌的叛军眼里，
这地方像天堂一样美丽。

就在那宜人的初秋早上，
李将军越过了山的屏障；

骑兵和步兵翻过了山岭，
迤逦地下山朝弗市推进。

四十面带有银星的国旗，
四十面带有红条的国旗，

原先在清晓的风中飘动，
中午时却都不见了影踪。

---

⑦ rebel horde：叛军，指南北战争中的南军。

⑧ Lee：Robert Edward Lee(1807—1870)，南军总司令。

⑨ winding['waindiŋ] down：蜿蜒而下，修饰上节的 marched。

⑩ Horse and foot：骑兵和步兵，全军。

⑪ 这里的 silver stars 和 crimson bars 的旗，即美国的星条旗，也是北军的旗帜。

⑫ saw not one＝did not see one；one 指一面星条旗。

Up rose old Barbara Frietchie then,
Bowed with her fourscore years and ten;[13]

Bravest of all in Frederick town,
She took up the flag the men hauled down;[14]

In her attic window the staff she set,[15]
To show that one heart was loyal yet.

Up the street came the rebel tread,
Stonewall Jackson riding ahead.[16]

Under his slouched hat left and right[17]
He glanced; the old flag met his sight.

"Halt!"—the dust-brown ranks stood fast.
"Fire!"—out blazed the rifle-blast.

It shivered the window, pane and sash;[18]
It rent the banner with seam and gash.[19]

Quick, as it fell from the broken staff,[20]
Dame Barbara snatched the silken scarf.[21]

---

[13]　本诗中的 Bowed 是过去分词,修饰 Barbara Frietchie; fourscore years and ten＝
　　　fourscore and ten years,用 20×4＋10 表示 90,是一种古旧的用法。

[14]　the flag the men hauled down:the flag 后省略 that 或 which;haul down one's flag
　　　是习语,扔下自己的旗子,有"投降"之意。这里用 men 含讽刺意,因为 Barbara 是位
　　　九十岁老妇。

[15]　the staff she set＝she set the staff.

[16]　Stonewall Jackson riding ahead:是独立结构,表示南军进军时的伴随情景。
　　　Stonewall Jackson,指南军副将 Thomas Jonathan Jackson(1824－1863),早先在
　　　Bull Run 一战中,坚守城池,制胜敌军,因而赢得 Stonewall(石墙,难以逾越的障
　　　碍)的称号。

芭芭拉·弗里奇这时站起，
九十岁的她伛偻着身躯；

弗城中最勇敢的人数她——
把男子们扯下的旗一拿；

从她顶楼上往窗外一伸，
以表明有颗心依然忠贞。

叛军在街上正朝这儿走，
"石壁"杰克逊骑马在前头。

低低帽檐下他东看西望，
这面旧旗正落入他眼光。

"立定！"——灰蒙蒙队伍顿时停。
"开火！"——响起来复枪的声音。

窗框和玻璃给震得颤动，
那国旗被打得千疮百孔。

绸旗刚从断旗杆上落下，
芭芭拉奶奶一把接住它。

---

⑰　left and right：状语，修饰下行的 glanced。

⑱　pane and sash：玻璃连窗框（全都受震），这里作状语。

⑲　rent：rend 的过去时。

⑳　Quick＝Quickly，修饰下一行的 snatched。

㉑　Dame：[古、诗]老太太。

She leaned far out on the window-sill,
And shook it forth with a royal will. ㉒

"Shoot, if you must, this old gray head, ㉓
But spare your country's flag," she said.

A shade of sadness, a blush of shame,
Over the face of the leader came; ㉔

The nobler nature within him stirred
To life at that woman's deed and word;

"Who touches a hair of yon gray head ㉕
Dies like a dog! March on !" he said. ㉖

All day long through Frederick street
Sounded the tread of marching feet:

All day long that free flag tost
Over the heads of the rebel host. ㉗

Ever its torn folds rose and fell
On the loyal winds that loved it well;

And through the hill-gaps sunset light
Shone over it with a warm good-night.

㉒　royal：庄严的，崇高的。

㉓　本行＝If you must shoot, shoot this old gray head.

㉔　本行＝Came over the face of the leader；the leader，指叛军头子 Jackson。

㉕　Who＝He who. yon：［古］＝yonder.

她从窗台上探出了身体，
坚定地挥动手中那面旗；

"要打就朝这白发头瞄准，"
她说，"你们的国旗可别碰。"

苦涩的阴影，羞惭的绯红，
掠过了这名叛将的面孔；

是这位年老妇女的言行，
把他心底里的良知唤醒；

他说，"谁敢动她一根白发，
我叫他死得像条狗！进发！"

整天里在那弗市的街上，
行进的脚步在沙沙作响；

整天里在那叛军的头上，
一面国旗在自由地飘荡。

旗虽破，忠贞的风仍爱它，
不断吹得它扬起又垂下；

斜阳从山口照耀在旗上，
像在热情地道晚安一样。

㉖　Dies＝Shall die.

㉗　host：[古] 军队；host['haust] 与上行的 tost[tɔst] 并不押韵，但看似押韵，称为"眼韵"(eye-rhyme)，下面第三节的 o'er 与 more 押的也是眼韵；tost，[古、诗] toss 的过去时。

Barbara Frietchie's work is o'er,
And the Rebel rides on his raids no more.

Honor to her! and let a tear
Fall, for her sake, on Stonewall's bier.

Over Barbara Frietchie's grave,
Flag of Freedom and Union, wave!

Peace and order and beauty draw
Round thy symbol of light and law;[28]

And ever the stars above look down
On thy stars below in Frederick town![29]

㉘　thy:指 Flag of Freedom and Union,即美国国旗而言。

㉙　thy stars:指旗上的星星。

芭芭拉的业绩已成往事，
叛军的袭掠也早已终止。

向她致敬！为了她也要让
泪滴落在"石壁"的墓地上。

自由和联邦之旗，请飘扬
在芭芭拉·弗里奇的墓上！

你是光明和法律的象征，
集和平、秩序和美于一身；

天上的繁星永远要俯望，
俯望你照耀弗市的星光。

ELDORADO[①]

Gaily bedight,[②]
A gallant knight,
In sunshine and in shadow,
Had journeyed long,
Singing a song,
In search of Eldorado.

But he grew old—
This knight so bold—
And o'er his heart a shadow
Fell as he found[③]
No spot of ground
That looked like Eldorado.

And, as his strength
Failed him at length,[④]
He met a pilgrim shadow—[⑤]
"Shadow," said he,
"Where can it be —
This land of Eldorado?"

"Over the mountains
Of the moon,
Down the valley of the shadow,[⑥]
Ride, boldly ride,"
The shade replied,—
"If you seek for Eldorado!"

---

① Eldorado ['eldɔ'raːdəu]：源出西班牙语 El Dorado，The Gilded 之意，十五世纪之际
人们相信南美洲北部存在着一个黄金国，后成为人们理想的象征。本诗反映了作者
痛感一生希望破灭的愁情。

② bedight：[古] 穿着，打扮，它的过去时和过去分词是 bedight 或 bedighted；这里的
bedight 是过去分词，=clad。

③ o'er his hear· a shadow/Fell＝a shadow fell over his heart.

爱尔多拉多

豪侠的骑士，
华丽的服饰，
任烈日如火、夜黑似墨，
他长途跋涉，
他引吭高歌，
一路寻找爱尔多拉多。

他虽是英豪，
却变得衰老，
一个阴影在他心头落，
因为他发现：
没一个地点
看来像那爱尔多拉多。

到得临了时，
他力竭精疲，
遇见一个游荡的魂魄：
"幽魂，"他讲，
"在什么地方——
我的那个爱尔多拉多？"

"翻过月亮里
一座座山岳，
走下那阴影里的幽壑，
驱马大胆找，"
幽魂回答道，
"要是想找爱尔多拉多。"

---

④ at length：最后，终于，是习语。

⑤ pilgrim shadow：指死神。

⑥ 这两行表明的全是虚无境界，犹如白居易《长恨歌》中所说的"上穷碧落下黄泉"。
请注意这首四节的小诗中，每节出现一个 shadow，意义各异，意境也随之步步阴
沉。第 1 节中的 shadow 是实义的阴荫，第 2 节中的是心上的阴影，第 3 节中的是死
神，第 4 节中的则是"死荫的幽谷"（据汉译《圣经》）。

THE BELLS[①]

Hear the sledges with the bells—

Silver bells!

What a world of merriment their melody foretells!

How they tinkle, tinkle, tinkle,

In the icy air of night!

While the stars that oversprinkle[②]

All the heavens, seem to twinkle

With a crystalline delight;[③]

Keeping time, time, time,[④]

In a sort of runic rhyme,[⑤]

To the tintinnabulation that so musically wells[⑥]

From the bells, bells, bells, bells,

Bells, bells, bells—

From the jingling and the tinkling of the bells.

---

① 本诗原有四节,共一百多行,分别吟咏银铃、金铃等,用拟声法(onomatopoeia)写来,被誉为绝唱。这里选译的是第 1 节,从头到底只听见清脆悦耳的叮当之声。

② oversprinkle＝sprinkle over.

③ crystalline:pure and clear 之意。

铃　铛

听听雪橇上的铃铛——

一个个银铃铛！

它们的曲调预示了多少的欢畅！

听它们的丁零丁零

响在夜色的霜风中！

而布满天空的星星，

像忽闪忽闪的水晶，

在表明它们的高兴：

像有着神秘的韵律一般，

它们有节拍地一闪一闪，

和着充满乐感的丁零当啷——

这乐音发自铃铛铃铛铃铛，

铃铛铃铛铃铛——

这乐音发自铃铛的丁丁当当。

---

④　本行后接 To the tintinnabulation，连用三个 time，表示连缀的节拍，三个 t 音的头韵
　　更令人如闻叮当之声；keep time to，合着……的拍子。

⑤　runic：来自 Rune，Rune 是古代北欧民族使用的字母，这种字母只有古代僧侣能懂，
　　秘不传授常人，久而久之，遂变得神秘莫测，因而 runic 有"神秘莫测的"之意。

⑥　tintinnabulation：叮当声，铃声。　wells：涌出，发出。

THE LAST LEAF[①]

I saw him once before,
As he passed by the door,
　　And again
The pavement stones resound,
As he totters o'er the ground
　　With his cane.

They say that in his prime,
Ere the pruning-knife of Time
　　Cut him down,[②]
Not a better man was found
By the Crier on his round[③]
　　Through the town.

But now he walks the streets,[④]
And he looks at all he meets
　　Sad and wan,[⑤]
And he shakes his feeble head,
That it seems as if he said,[⑥]
　　"They are gone."

The mossy marbles rest
On the lips that he has prest
　　In their bloom,[⑦]
And the names he loved to hear
Have been carved for many a year
　　On the tomb.

---

① 据称作者曾说，这首诗是他在波士顿街头看到一个据说是革命军人的老人，有感而作。这人名叫 Thomas Melville(1751—1832)，是独立战争中的英雄。

② 本行有两种意义，一是"夺去他的生命"，一是"消损他的健康"，此处取后一义。

③ Crier：巡行街道宣读公告的人，＝town crier。

最后一片树叶

他曾走过我门前，
　　就那次被我看见；
　　　石路上现在
　　又传来脚步声响，
　　那是他拄着拐杖，
　　　蹒跚地走来。

据说在他的壮年——
　　岁月那把修枝剪
　　　没把他剪下——
　　传告员跑遍这城，
　　发现最出色的人
　　　那就得数他。

现在他走在街上，
　　看到一切都打量——
　　　脸憔悴悲哀，
　　脑袋无力地摇摇，
　　那神情像是说道：
　　　"他们已不在。"

长着青苔的石下，
　　埋着他吻过的她——
　　　好两片樱唇；
　　他所爱听的姓名、
　　在多年之前已经
　　　刻成了碑文。

---

① walks the streets：在街上走走，是习语；这个习语也常作"做妓女"解。

⑤ Sad and wan：指上行的 he，不是指更贴近这两个形容词的 all he meets。

⑥ That = So that.

⑦ In their bloom：(嘴唇)正如盛开的花朵般红润。

My grandmama has said,—
Poor old lady, she is dead
      long ago,—
That he had a Roman nose,[8]
And his cheek was like a rose
      In the snow;

But now his nose is thin,
And it rests upon his chin
      Like a staff,
And a crook is in his back,
And a melancholy crack[9]
      In his laugh.

I know it is a sin
For me to sit and grin
      At him here;
But the old three-cornered hat,[10]
And the breeches, and all that,[11]
      Are so queer!

And if I should live to be
The last leaf upon the tree,
      In the spring,
Let them smile, as I do now,
At the old forsaken bough
      Where I cling.

---

⑧ Roman nose：以细长为美的罗马人的鼻子，常译作"鹰爪鼻"。

⑨ crack：粗哑的嗓音，破壳声，后省略 is。

我祖母曾经说起——
好老太早已去世，
　　真叫人伤悲——
他有神气的鼻梁，
脸颊曾像雪地上
　　一朵红玫瑰。

现在鼻子已精瘦，
耷拉在下巴上头，
　　样子像短棍；
他的背有点像弓，
伤感的笑声之中
　　掺着干咳声。

我知道这是罪过：
笑嘻嘻这里一坐，
　　看着他走来；
可那古派三角帽、
紧身短裤等一套，
　　也实在是怪！

要是我此生绵绵，
成了最后的叶瓣，
　　那么春天时
随人家也这样笑：
笑我依恋地拥抱
　　老迈的空枝。

⑩　three-cornered hat：古时正式服装中的一种三角帽，但诗人写此诗时已过时。

⑪　breeches：马裤，宫廷礼裤。and all that：等等，诸如此类，是习语。

MY AUNT

My aunt! my dear unmarried aunt!
    Long years have o'er her flown;①
Yet still she strains the aching clasp
    That binds her virgin zone;②
I know it hurts her,—though she looks
    As cheerful as she can;
Her waist is ampler than her life,
    For life is but a span. ③

My aunt! my poor deluded aunt!④
    Her hair is almost gray;
Why will she train that winter curl⑤
    In such a spring-like way?
How can she lay her glasses down,
    And say she reads as well,
When through a double convex lens⑥
    She just makes out to spell?

Her father—grandpapa! forgive
    This erring lip its smiles—⑦
Vowed she should make the finest girl⑧
    Within a hundred miles;
He sent her to a stylish school;⑨
    'T was in her thirteenth June;⑩
And with her, as the rules required,
    "Two towels and a spoon. "

---

① have o'er her flown＝have flown over her.
② zone：[古、诗] 腰带；virgin zone，也作 maiden zone，是处女的象征。
③ life is but a span：谚语，犹言"人生如朝露"。
④ deluded：受蒙蔽的。这表明诗人对她所受的教育有看法。
⑤ winter curl：冬天的鬈发，谓鬈发白如冬天的冰霜。

我 的 姑 姑

姑姑！我亲爱的未嫁姑姑！
　　多少年打身旁飞走，
她却还不顾疼痛地使劲，
　　把处女的腰带紧扣；
我知道她疼，尽管看起来
　　她依然是快乐如常；
她腰围大于她生命的长度，
　　因为人生只一拃长。

姑姑！受蒙蔽的可怜姑姑！
　　头发已几乎都灰白，
为什么把冬雪似的鬓发
　　打点得春日般光彩？
她带上前凸后凸的镜片，
　　才勉强能辨字拼读，
怎么取下了眼镜竟还说：
　　不戴也照样能看书？

她爸爸（爷爷呀！请你原谅
　　这犯上的嘴在微笑）
曾断言：方圆三百里之内，
　　将数这闺女最出挑；
她到了十三岁那年六月，
　　被送进时髦的学校，
而且还按照校规的要求，
　　"带茶匙加毛巾两条。"

---

⑥　double convex lens：双凸面透镜，也称 biconvex lens。

⑦　This erring lip：(我)这说错了话的嘴，指应称呼"爷爷"而没规矩地说了"她爸爸"。

⑧　make：成为。

⑨　He sent：sent 的宾语有三，一是 her，另两个是末行的 Two towels 和 a spoon。

⑩　'T＝It. 这一行是插入语，可当它前后有括弧或破折号。

They braced my aunt against a board,[11]
  To make her straight and tall;
They laced her up, they starved her down,
  To make her light and small,
They pinched her feet, they singed her hair,[12]
  They screwed it up with pins;—
Oh, never mortal suffered more
  In penance for her sins.

So, when my precious aunt was done,
  My grandsire brought her back;
(By daylight, lest some rabid youth
  Might follow on the track;)[13]
"Ah!" said my grandsire, as he shook
  Some powder in his pan,[14]
"What could this lovely creature do
  Against a desperate man!"

Alas! nor chariot, nor barouche,[15]
  Nor bandit cavalcade,
Tore from the trembling father's arms
  His all-accomplished maid.
For her how happy had it been![16]
  And heaven had spared to me[17]
To see one sad, ungathered rose
  On my ancestral tree.

---

⑪　braced my aunt against a board：用一块板缚在我姑姑身上，使她身子挺直。这里的
　　board＝backboard，见萨克雷名著《名利场》第一章，杨必译本中作"背板"。

⑫　pinched her feet：给她穿小鞋子，为的是要她的脚小巧有样，与我国旧时的裹足无独
　　有偶。

⑬　follow on the track：跟踪，钉梢。

她们把她紧扎在木板上，
　　要使她背直个儿高；
她们束她腰，让她饿肚子，
　　要使她轻盈又娇小；
她们给她的鞋小，用发钳
　　烫焦她头发往上扭；
啊，即使为了赎罪，也没人
　　在这种煎熬里苦修。

好姑姑这样给整治完毕，
　　爷爷就接她回家中；
（接她在白天，免得碰上
　　愣小子在后面跟踪；）
"唉！"爷爷他一边这么说，
　　一边给火枪装火药，
"我千娇百媚的闺女碰上
　　亡命徒可怎么得了！"

唉！没轻便马车和大马车，
　　没成帮的骑马孽障
从那父亲惊颤的怀里抢走
　　这尽善尽美的姑娘。
老天如那样办，她多幸福！
　　而我也就不会看见：
一朵没摘去的郁郁玫瑰
　　挂我世系树的枝间。

⑭　shook some powder in his pan：在他的(枪的)火药池里撒进些火药；pan，旧式枪的火药池。

⑮　nor…，nor…：[古、诗]＝neither…nor…。

⑯　本行＝How happy it would have been for her，虚拟语气，省略条件从句 if she had been torn away from her father's arms。

⑰　spared to me＝spared for me。

THE FUGITIVE SLAVES

Ye sorrowing people! who from bondage fly,

And cruel laws that men against you make,—

Think not that none there are who hear your cry

And for yourselves and children thought will take. [1]

Though now bowed down with sorrow and with fear, [2]

Lift up your heads! for you are not alone;

Some christian hearts are left your flight to cheer, [3]

Some human hearts not wholly turned to stone; [4]

God to His angels shall give strictest charge,

And in their hands they'll bear you safe from harm,

Where in a freer land you'll roam at large, [5]

Nor dread pursuit, nor start at each alarm;

Till in His time you shall return again, [6]

No more to feel man's wrath or dread his chain. [7]

---

[1]　本行＝And will take thought for yourselves and your children. take thought for, 为……担心, 关心, 与 hear your cry 并列。

[2]　Though now bowed down＝Though now you are bowed down.

[3]　your flight to cheer＝to cheer your flight.

[4]　not wholly turned to stone: 承上行, ＝are not wholly turned to stone.

逃 亡 的 奴 隶

悲苦的人们哪！你们逃出奴役，
逃出强加于你们的苛法严刑——
别以为没人会听见你们哭泣，
会为你们和你们的子女担心。
现在虽被悲伤和恐惧压弯腰，
但昂起头来！因为你们不孤单；
还有些基督徒在为逃亡叫好，
有些人的心还没像石头一般；
上帝会给天使极严格的吩咐，
他们将会把你们安然无恙地
送到你们可自由来去的乡土，
不再为追捕担心，闻警而战栗；
直到上帝到时候唤你们回去，
不再为人的暴虐和锁链恐惧。

---

⑤　at large：不受拘束地，逍遥自在地，是习语。

⑥　按照基督教的说法，到世界末日，耶稣将重新降临人间，已经死去的人都将复活，受
"末日审判"，坏人下地狱，好人上天堂。

⑦　这是一首莎士比亚式十四行诗，每行是十个音节构成的五音步，韵式为 abab cdcd
efef gg。

TODAY

I live but in the present,—where art thou?^①

Hast thou a home in some past, future year?

I call to thee from every leafy bough,

But thou art far away and canst not hear.

Each flower lifts up its red or yellow head,

And nods to thee as thou art passing by:

Hurry not on, but stay thine anxious tread,^②

And thou shalt live with me, for there am I.

The stream that murmurs by thee,—heed its voice,

Nor stop thine ear; 'tis I that bid it flow;^③

And thou with its glad waters shalt rejoice,

And of the life I live within them know.

And hill, and grove, and flowers, and running stream,

When thou dost live with them shall look more fair;^④

And thou awake as from a cheating dream,

The life today with me and mine to share.^⑤

---

① thou：指拟人化的作为本诗主题的"今天"。

② thine=thy，此处因后接元音开头的 anxious，故用 thine；下节第 2 行中 thine ear 同。

③ Nor：在肯定句后＝And not；Nor stop thine ear＝And do not stop your ear.

今　天

我只是生活在现在，你在哪里？
你在过去或将来可有一个家？
我从一切繁枝茂叶里呼唤你，
但是，远远的你听不见我的话。

一朵朵红或黄的花仰起面庞，
向经过身边的你点着头示意：
停下你焦急的脚步，可别匆忙，
你便同这儿的我生活在一起。

听听你身旁流过的潺潺小溪，
别塞上耳朵；要它流淌的是我；
你会为那欢快的溪水而欣喜，
会懂得我置身于其中的生活。

山丘、树丛、花朵和流淌的小河，
有你生活在一起就显得更漂亮；
你会像从骗人的梦中醒来，同我
和我的亲人把今天的生活分享。

---

④　shall look：主语为上行的 hill，grove，flowers，stream。

⑤　本行＝To share the life today with me and mine；today 这里是副词，不是拟人化的大写开首的 Today；mine 指我的亲人们。

TO THE DANDELION[①]

Dear common flower, that grow'st beside the way,
Fringing the dusty road with harmless gold,
　　First pledge of blithesome May,[②]
Which children pluck, and full of pride uphold,
　　High-hearted buccaneers, o'erjoyed that they[③]
An Eldorado in the grass have found,[④]
　　Which not the rich earth's ample round[⑤]
　　May match in wealth, thou art more dear to me
Than all the prouder summer-blooms may be.

Gold such as thine ne'er drew the Spanish prow[⑥]
Through the primeval hush of Indian seas,[⑦]
　　Nor wrinkled the lean brow
Of age, to rob the lover's heart of ease;[⑧]
　　'Tis the Spring's largess, which she scatters now
To rich and poor alike, with lavish hand,[⑨]
　　Though most hearts never understand
　　To take it at God's value, but pass by[⑩]
The offered wealth with unrewarded eye.[⑪]

---

① Dandelion['dændilaiən],这个词是从法语 dent de lion(狮子的牙齿)而来,因其花形相似。

② 本行是首行 flower 的同位语。pledge:信物,象征物。

③ High-hearted buccaneers [bʌkə'niəz]:是上行 children 的同位语;buccaneers,十七八世纪西班牙所属西印度群岛一带洋面上横行的海盗,这里戏称那些兴高采烈的孩子们。

④ Eldorado:见前 Allan Poe 所作 Eldorado 篇的题解。

⑤ round:圆形物,地球的圆形的范围。

致 蒲 公 英

可爱又常见的花呀长在路旁，
你为灰蒙蒙的路镶无害金边，
　　先送来五月的欢畅；
孩子摘你，自豪地把你举向天；
　　这些无忧的盗花者欣喜若狂，
因为在草中发现一个黄金国——
　　　财富比丰饶的世界还多；
　　你呀，在我的眼中你最为亲密，
　　夏日的所有娇花都难同你比。

　　你这黄金没招致西班牙船舰
驶过西印度海域原始的寂静，
　　　也没使老人的瘦脸
皱起来，使情人的心不得安宁；
　　这是春日的恩赐，对富人穷汉
她现在同样慷慨地把你分送；
　　　尽管多数人从来都不懂
　　其真正价值，只是毫不感恩地
　　在这天赐的财富旁一掠而过。

---

⑥　prow：船头，诗中常指"船"。

⑦　Indian seas：指西印度海域。

⑧　to rob the lover's heart of ease：夺去情人心中的安逸，使有情人不得安宁；rob sb.
　　of sth.：夺去某人的东西。

⑨　rich and poor＝the rich and the poor.

⑩　understand/To take it at God's value：懂得按照上帝对它珍重的程度珍重它。

⑪　unrewarded eye：没有领悟其价值的眼睛。

Thou art my tropics and mine Italy;[12]
To look at thee unlocks a warmer clime;
    The eyes thou givest me
Are in the heart, and heed not space or time:
    Not in mid June the golden-cuirassed bee
Feels a more summer-like warm ravishment[13]
    In the white lily's breezy tent,
    His fragrant Sybaris, than I, when first[14]
From the dark green thy yellow circles burst. [15]

Then think I of deep shadows on the grass,[16]
Of meadows where in sun the cattle graze,
    Where, as the breezes pass,
The gleaming rushes lean a thousand ways,
    Of leaves that slumber in a cloudy mass,
Or whiten in the wind, of waters blue
    That from the distance sparkle through
    Some woodland gap, and of a sky above,
Where one white cloud like a stray lamb doth move.

My childhood's earliest thoughts are linked with thee;
The sight of thee calls back the robin's song,[17]
    Who, from the dark old tree
Beside the door, sang clearly all day long,
    And I, secure in childish piety,
Listened as if I heard an angel sing
    With news from heaven, which he could bring
    Fresh every day to my untainted ears
When birds and flowers and I were happy peers.

---

⑫ mine:[古]＝my, 这里因后面接元音开始的 Italy 而用 mine。

⑬ Not...:这两行因 Not 放句首而倒装,正常词序是 The golden-cuirassed [-kwi′ræst]
    bee does not feel in mid June a more summer-like warm ravishment (than I)。

⑭ sybaris:[′sibəris]是意大利南部一古都,以奢侈享乐闻名;这里是 tent 的同位语。

你是我的热带,是我的意大利;
看着你,就开启温暖地带一片;
　　　你所给予我的眼力
在我心中,它不管地点或时间:
　　　当你的黄球初开在绿草丛里,
即使裹着黄金甲的仲夏蜜蜂
　　　进了风中百合花的帐篷——
　　　进了它这芬芳温暖的安乐窝——
　　　它对销魂之夏的感受不如我。

于是我想到落到草上的浓影;
想到牛群吃草的阳光下牧场,
　　　在那里,每一阵微风
叫蒲苇千姿百态地低伏、闪亮;
　　　想到葱郁一团的树叶入了梦
或风吹一片白,想到远处碧水
　　　透过林地的空处露光辉;
　　　我还想到头上的蓝天,在那里,
　　　像离群羔羊,一朵白云在飘移。

我最早的童年回忆同你相关:
看到你我便想起知更鸟歌唱,
　　　它在门旁的老树间,
在浓密树荫里整天歌声嘹亮,
　　　而无忧的我怀着孩子的虔诚
凝神倾听,像听见上天的消息
　　　被天使唱出,它还有能力
　　　每天把新奇带进我纯洁耳朵——
　　　那时候我和花鸟朋友多快活!

---

⑮　circles:圆形的花。

⑯　think I of =I think of ,连用五个of,分别以 shadows、meadows、leaves、waters 和 a sky 为介词宾语,构成这一诗节的全部内容,余皆这些宾语的修饰语。

⑰　the robin's song,/Who... =the song of the robin, who....

How like a prodigal doth nature seem,
When thou, for all thy gold, so common art![⑱]
   Thou teachest me to deem
More sacredly of every human heart,
  Since each reflects in joy its scanty gleam
Of heaven, and could some wondrous secret show,
    Did we but pay the love we owe,[⑲]
  And with a child's undoubting wisdom look
On all these living pages of God's book.

⑱ 本行＝When thou art so common for all thy gold；art，[古]be 的现在时单数第二人称，＝are。

自然，多像是挥金如土的浪子，
尽管你满身是金，却如此普通！
　　　你给予我的教导是：
把每一颗人心看得更神圣，
　　因为欢乐的心凭一点儿闪熠
反映出天意，而我们只要偿清
　　该付的爱，以孩子的诚心
翻看上帝这本书的生动书页，
神妙的奥义就会显露出一些。

STANZAS ON FREEDOM

Men! whose boast it is that ye[①]

Come of fathers brave and free,

If there breathe on earth a slave,

Are ye truly free and brave?

If ye do not feel the chain,

When it works a brother's pain,[②]

Are ye not base slaves indeed,

Slaves unworthy to be freed?

Women! who shall one day bear[③]

Sons to breathe New England air,

If ye hear, without a blush,

Deeds to make the roused blood rush

Like red lava through your veins,

For your sisters now in chains,

Answer! are ye fit to be

Mothers of the brave and free?

---

① whose boast it is that...：在这结构中不可分 it ，因为它＝it is whose boast that...。

② works：及物动词，造成。

咏　自　由

男子们！你们为出身夸口，
说自己的先人勇敢自由！
如果有一个奴隶在人间，
你们还算是真自由勇敢？
让兄弟感到痛苦的链条
如果说你们竟感觉不到，
你们岂不是下贱的奴才——
根本就不配被解放出来？

女子们！你们迟早将生育
吸新英格兰空气的子女，
对你们在枷锁中的姐妹
有些使热血怒涌的行为——
使血像岩浆流在血管中——
如果你们竟听了脸不红，
那你们说：是否配当一名
勇敢自由的孩子的母亲？

---

③　bear：(妇女)生(孩子)。

Is true Freedom but to break④

Fetters for our own dear sake,

And, with leathern hearts, forget⑤

That we owe mankind a debt?

No! true freedom is to share

All the chains our brothers wear,

And, with heart and hand, to be ⑥

Earnest to make others free!

They are slaves who fear to speak⑦

For the fallen and the weak;

They are slaves who will not choose

Hatred, scoffing, and abuse,⑧

Rather than in silence shrink

From the truth they needs must think;⑨

They are slaves who dare not be

In the right with two or three.⑩

---

④　but＝only.

⑤　leathern hearts：皮革般坚硬的心，犹言"铁石心肠"。

⑥　with heart and hand：全心全意地，有时不用 with，同样作状语。

⑦　本行＝They who fear to speak are slaves；英国谚语 All is not gold that glitters 是同样的结构。

真正的自由，竟只是为了
爱我们自己才砸断镣铐？
只是听凭我们麻木的心
忘掉我们对人类的责任？
不！真正的自由就是分担
兄弟们身上的一切锁链，
就是尽心竭力地去奋斗，
去帮助其他人争得自由！

只配做奴隶的人才害怕
为那些倒下者、弱者说话；
他们准知道什么是正理，
可退缩在一旁吞声忍气，
不敢嘲笑辱骂也不敢恨，
真正的奴隶就是这种人；
两三个人一起维护正义，
连这也不敢的人是奴隶。

---

⑧ Hatred，scoffing，and abuse：都是指对敌人，就是鲁迅所说的"横眉怒对千夫指"的
  态度。
⑨ needs must：必须；这里的 needs 是副词。
⑩ be /In the right：站在正义的一边，是习语。

ALADDIN[①]

When I was a beggarly boy,
 And lived in a cellar damp,[②]
I had not a friend nor a toy,
 But I had Aladdin's lamp;
When I could not sleep for the cold,
 I had fire enough in my brain,
And builded, with roofs of gold,[③]
 My beautiful castles in Spain![④]

Since then I have toiled day and night,
 I have money and power good store,[⑤]
But I'd give all my lamps of silver bright
 For the one that is mine no more;[⑥]
Take, Fortune, whatever you choose,
 You gave, and may snatch again;[⑦]
I have nothing 't would pain me to lose,[⑧]
 For I own no more castles in Spain!

---

①   Aladdin：阿拉丁，《天方夜谭》故事《阿拉丁和神灯》中的主人公。
②   cellar damp ＝damp cellar，倒装是为与隔行的 lamp 押韵。
③   builded＝built.
④   castles in Spain：空中楼阁。
⑤   money and power good store＝a good store of money and power.

阿　拉　丁

我是个穷苦孩子的时候，
　　潮湿的地窖是我房间，
我没有玩具也没有朋友，
　　却有阿拉丁的灯一盏；
有时我冷得觉也睡不着，
　　可脑海中火样的热情
造着缥缈的西班牙城堡，
　　堡上有美丽的金屋顶！

从那时候起我日夜苦干，
　　我现在有了钱和地位；
可情愿拿全部银灯去换，
　　把不再是我的灯换回；
拣你要的取走，命运女神，
　　你给的，你有权再拿掉，
任你拿什么，我也不心疼——
　　既没有了西班牙城堡！

---

⑥　the one ＝ the lamp.

⑦　这两行可理解为彼此独立的，也可理解为有从属关系，即后一行前面省略关系代词
　　That，它的先行词是 whatever(或谓 whatever 中的 what)，意思是："幸福之神啊，凡
　　是你给了可以再收回去的一切，你要什么就拿什么。"

⑧　本行中 nothing 后省略 that 或 which，作它引起的从句中的 lose 的宾语。

A NOISELESS PATIENT SPIDER

A noiseless patient spider,

I mark'd where on a little promontory it stood isolated,①

Mark'd how to explore the vacant vast surrounding,②

It launch'd forth filament, filament, filament, out of itself,

Ever unreeling them, ever tirelessly speeding them.③

And you O my soul where you stand,④

Surrounded, detached, in measureless oceans of space,

Ceaselessly musing, venturing, throwing, seeking

    the spheres to connect them,

Till the bridge you will need be form'd,

    till the ductile anchor hold,

Till the gossamer thread you fling catch somewhere, O my

    soul.⑤

---

① promontory：岬，海角，这里比喻三面临空之处。

② how：接下行 It launch'd forth...；紧接在 how 后面的不定式短语 to explore... 是
插入的目的状语，修饰 launch'd。

一只不出声的耐心蜘蛛

一只不出声的耐心蜘蛛，

我注意到它独处于一个小小的孤岛，

注意到它怎样在那空阔的环境里探索，

它抛出自己体内的细丝，细丝，细丝，

一直在放出它们，一直在不倦地把它们投出。

我的心灵哦，你所在之处

也被无可度量的茫茫空间团团包围，

你不停地思索，试探，投出，搜寻着各个领域以

　　　建立联系，

直到你需要的桥被建成，直到你可展延的柔韧

　　　的锚锚住，

直到你甩出的轻灵游丝粘上某处，我的心灵哦！

---

③ 第 3 行 vacant vast 的头韵 v（译文用双声词"空阔"），第 4 行叠用三个 filament，和
　第 5 行 unreeling 和 speeding 的两个[iː]音，都给人以蛛丝连绵不绝之感；speed-
　ing：发射，放送。

④ you O my soul：是呼语，整节就是这个呼语和它的修饰语，结尾重复一声这个呼语。

⑤ Till：连用三个 till，它们所引起的从句中均用原形动词作谓语动词。

I HEAR AMERICA SINGING

I hear America singing, the varied carols I hear,[1]
Those of mechanics, each one singing his as it should be
    blithe and strong,[2]
The carpenter singing his as he measures his plank or beam,
The mason singing his as he makes ready for work, or leaves
    off work,
The boatman singing what belongs to him in his boat, the
    deckhand singing on the steamboat deck,
The shoemaker singing as he sits on his bench, the hatter
    singing as he stands,
The wood-cutter's song, the plowboy's on his way in the
    morning, or at noon intermission or at sundown,
The delicious singing of the mother, or of the young wife at
    work, or of the girl sewing or washing,
Each singing what belongs to him or her and to none else,
The day what belongs to the day—at night the party of
    young fellows, robust, friendly,[3]
Singing with open mouths their strong melodious songs.

---

①   the varied carols I hear =I hear the varied carols.

②   Those = The carols; 同一行中 his = his carol; it = the carol.

我听见亚美利加在歌唱

我听见亚美利加在歌唱,我听见的欢歌多种多样,
机匠的歌是该愉快雄壮,他们一个个就这样把自己的
　　歌高唱,
木工唱着他的歌,一边量着他的木板或横梁,
石匠唱着他的歌,准备着上工或下班,
船工在他的船上唱着属于自己的歌,甲板水手在汽船
　　甲板上歌唱,
坐在长凳上的鞋匠在唱,站着的帽匠在唱,
伐木工在唱,犁地的小伙子在唱——不管是早晨下地
　　时,中午歇工时还是日落时,
甜美的歌声来自母亲,来自干活的年轻主妇,来自缝缝
　　洗洗的姑娘,
人人在唱属于自己、不属于其他任何人的歌,
白天唱属于白天的歌——到了夜晚,一群强健而友好
　　的年轻人
张大着嘴在唱,唱他们雄壮又悦耳的歌。

---

③　The day what belongs to the day：承上行，= The day singing what belongs to the day.

WHEN I HEARD THE LEARN'D ASTRONOMER

When I heard the learn'd astronomer,[①]

When the proofs, the figures, were ranged in columns
before me,

When I was shown the charts and diagrams, to add, divide,
and measure them,

When I sitting heard the astronomer where he lectured with
much applause in the lecture-room,

How soon unaccountable I became tired and sick,[②]

Till rising and gliding out I wander'd off by myself,

In the mystical moist night-air, and from time to time,

Look'd up in perfect silence at the stars.

---

① learn'd [ləːnd] = 形容词 learned ['ləːnid]，这里为音韵需要缩略一个音节。

当我听着博学的天文学家

当我听着博学的天文学家，

当证据和数据一排排开列在我面前，

当他展示图表和图解，要加、要除、要予以度量，

当我坐在讲堂里，听天文学家演讲和听众热烈鼓掌，

我很快就莫名其妙地感到疲乏、厌倦，

直到我站起身溜出讲堂，一个人信步走去，

在那玄妙而湿润的夜晚空气里时不时

绝无声息地把星斗仰望。

② unaccountable = unaccountably.

BATTLE HYMN OF THE REPUBLIC[①]

Mine eyes have seen the glory of the coming of the Lord:
He is trampling out the vintage where the grapes of wrath are
    stored;[②]
He hath loosed the fateful lightning of his terrible swift
    sword:
    His truth is marching on.

I have seen him in the watch-fires of a hundred circling camps;
They have builded him an altar in the evening dews and damps;
I can read his righteous sentence by the dim and flaring lamps:
    His day is marching on.

I have read a fiery gospel, writ in burnished rows of steel:
"As ye deal with my contemners, so with you my grace shall
    deal;
Let the Hero, born of woman, crush the serpent with his heel,
    Since God is marching on."[③]

He has sounded forth the trumpet that shall never call retreat;
He is sifting out the hearts of men before his judgment-seat:
O, be swift, my soul, to answer him! be jubilant, my feet!
    Our God is marching on .

In the beauty of the lilies Christ was born across the sea,
With a glory in his bosom that transfigures you and me;
As he died to make men holy, let us die to make men free,
    While God is marching on.

---

① 本诗是南北战争期间流行于北军中的一支爱国歌曲;作者于 1861 年访问北军时,
   听到士兵们唱着当时流行的进步歌曲《约翰·布朗的遗体》,深有所感,遂按其曲
   调,写下此诗,发表于《大西洋月刊》,备受欢迎,流行至今。

共和国战歌

我的眼看见过我主来临时的辉煌光灿：
他正把藏有"忿怒葡萄"的整批收成踩烂；
他抽出可怕的迅猛之剑，发出致命闪电：
　　　　他的真理在行进。

我见过他，见他在周围百座军营营火里；
他们在夜露和潮气中为他把圣坛建起；
我能凭忽闪、幽暗的灯读他正义的词句：
　　　　他的时代在行进。

我读过一列列擦亮的钢写的火样福音：
"我是否恩典你，看你如何待藐视我的人；
让女子生养的英雄把那蛇踩死在脚跟，
　　　　因为上帝在行进。"

他吹响的喇叭永远也不会叫人们后撤；
他审判座前那些人的心，他正在筛分着：
我的灵魂哪，快答复他！脚啊，该欢乐！
　　　　我们的上帝在行进。

大海那边，基督降生在百合花的美丽中，
他胸中的荣耀使你我变得与从前不同；
他为使人圣洁而死，我们为解放人而终，
　　　　因为上帝在行进。

---

② grapes of wrath：忿怒的葡萄，意指骚动不宁的根源或愤慨暴乱的种子，见《圣经·
新约·启示录》第 14 章 19—20 节。

③ 这段文字出处待考。

Frederick G. Tuckerman   80

UNDER THE MOUNTAIN,
AS WHEN FIRST I KNEW ①

Under the mountain, as when first I knew②
Its low dark roof and chimney creeper-twined,③
The red house stands; and yet my footsteps find,
Vague in the walks, waste balm and feverfew.④
But they are gone: no soft-eyed sisters trip⑤
Across the porch or lintels; where, behind,
The mother sat, sat knitting with pursed lip.
The house stands vacant in its green recess,
Absent of beauty as a broken heart.⑥
The wild rain enters, and the sunset wind
Sighs in the chambers of their loveliness⑦
Or shakes the pane—and in the silent noons
The glass falls from the window, part by part,
And ringeth faintly in the grassy stones.⑧

---

① 这是一首十四行诗，但它的韵脚排列除开头四行为 abba 外，后面十行尽管行行有韵，但排列比较自由。
② as when I knew... = as the red house was when I knew...; as the red house was 修饰第 3 行的 The red house stands。
③ chimney creeper-twined = creeper-twined chimney.
④ find, / Vague in the walks, waste balm and feverfew: find 的宾语是 waste balm and feverfew, vague in the walks 修饰 waste balm and feverfew.

那幢红房子仍旧矗立在山脚旁

那幢红房子仍旧矗立在山脚旁，
低低的黑屋顶，带爬山虎的烟囱，
宛如我初见的模样；脚下的路中，
是些恹恹无主的小白菊、白壳杨。
可人去屋空：门廊或者门窗里
没了眼盈盈的姐妹倩影，后面，
也没嘟着嘴的母亲坐着打毛线。
房子空荡荡坐落在绿色山凹里——
已丧失了所有的美，像碎了的心。
狂乱的雨儿打进去，落日时的风
在那些房间里为其可爱而悲叹，
或者摇撼着窗户——寂静的午间，
一块块碎破璃从窗上掉落地上，
在长草的石板上幽幽哐嘟作响。

---

⑤　they are gone：他们（指原先住在这里的人们）不在了。

⑥　Absent of：缺乏……的，没有……的。

⑦　本行 = Sighs of their (the chambers') loveliness in the chambers，在这些房间里哀叹它们的可爱。

⑧　ringeth ['riŋiθ] = rings，为抑扬格的需要增加一个"抑"音节。

AND CHANGE WITH HURRIED HAND
HAS SWEPT THESE SCENES①

And change with hurried hand has swept these scenes:

The woods have fallen, across the meadow-lot

The hunter's trail and trap-path is forgot,

And fire has drunk the swamps of evergreens;

Yet for a moment let my fancy plant

These autumn hills again: the wild dove's haunt,②

The wild deer's walk. In golden umbrage shut,③

The Indian river runs, Quonecktacut!④

Here, but a lifetime back, where falls tonight⑤

Behind the curtained pane a sheltered light

On buds of rose or vase of violet

Aloft upon the marble mantel set,

Here in the forest-heart, hung blackening⑥

The wolfbait on the bush beside the spring.

---

① 这也是一首十四行诗,其韵脚的排列比较特别, 是 abba ccdd eeff gg。

② the wild dove's haunt: 可理解为前面省略 with; 下行的 The wild deer's walk 同。

③ In golden umbrage ['ʌmbridʒ] shut = shut in golden umbrage; umbrage, 成荫的簇叶。

④ Quonecktacut, 即 Connecticut, 康涅狄格河。

变化之手匆匆扫过这些景致

变化之手匆匆扫过这些景致：
树林已被采伐；那片牧草地上，
猎径和放捕机的小道被遗忘；
沼泽地里的常青树被火吞噬。
但让我的想象暂时把这秋日
山岭重描：那是野鸽子栖息地、
野鹿的山道。金色的树叶遮着
奔流的印第安河水：匡耐特克！
拉上帘子的窗后，灯罩下的光
今夜落在高高的云石炉台上，
照亮玫瑰花蕾或瓶中紫罗兰；
可这地方仅仅在一世人以前，
在森林中央，灌木丛挨着河水——
给狼吃的饵挂在那里在变黑。

---

⑤ but a lifetime back：仅仅在人的一生的时间之前，即不到一百年光景之前。where falls...：where 所引起的状语从句修饰 Here；falls 的主语是下一行的 a sheltered light。

⑧ Here：重复前面第 9 行的 Here，因前面那个 Here 拖着一个很长的从句，距离它所修饰的 hung 太远。hung：主语是下行的 The wolfbait。

DIRGE FOR A SOLDIER

Close his eyes; his work is done!
　　What to him is friend or foeman,
Rise of moon, or set of sun,
　　Hand of man, or kiss of woman?
　　Lay him low, lay him low,
　　In the clover or the snow!
　　What cares he? He cannot know:[①]
　　　　Lay him low!

As man may, he fought his fight,[②]
　　Proved his truth by his endeavor;
Let him sleep in solemn night,
　　Sleep forever and forever.
　　Lay him low, lay him low,
　　In the clover or the snow!
　　What cares he? He cannot know:
　　　　Lay him low!

---

① What cares he? = What does he care? 这是个反问句,意即"他不介意"。

给一名军人的挽歌

合上他眼睛；他已干完活！

　　男人的手或女人的亲嘴、

朋友或敌人、月出或日落，

　　对于他这些都已无所谓！

　　深深埋下他，深深埋下他，

　　埋他在积雪或三叶草下！

　　他无知无觉，有什么牵挂？

　　　　深深埋下他！

他曾经奋勇地拼命厮杀，

　　凭努力把他的忠诚证实；

让他在庄严的夜里睡吧，

　　让他的这一觉永无尽期。

　　深深埋下他，深深埋下他，

　　埋他在积雪或三叶草下！

　　他无知无觉，有什么牵挂？

　　　　深深埋下他！

② As man may：如人类所能做到那样地，尽力地。参考习语 as best one may。

Fold him in his country's stars,[③]

　　Roll the drum and fire the volley!

What to him are all our wars,

　　What but death bemocking folly?[④]

　　Lay him low, lay him low,

　　In the clover or the snow!

　　What cares he? He cannot know：

　　　　Lay him low!

Leave him to God's watching eye,

　　Trust him to the hand that made him,

Mortal love weeps idly by：[⑤]

　　God alone has power to aid him.

　　Lay him low, lay him low,

　　In the clover or the snow!

　　What cares he? He cannot know：

　　　　Lay him low!

---

③　his country's stars：指美国的星条旗。

④　本行承上行 = What are all our wars to him but death bemocking folly? but = except.

用他的星条旗把他裹严，

　　为他敲起鼓和鸣放排炮！

我们的战争已同他无关——

　　只是死神对愚行的嘲笑！

　　深深埋下他，深深埋下他，

　　埋他在积雪或三叶草下！

　　他无知无觉，有什么牵挂？

　　　　深深埋下他！

留下他让上帝给以关注，

　　交他到曾创造他的手中；

只有上帝能给予他帮助，

　　人的爱在旁哭哭没有用。

　　深深埋下他，深深埋下他，

　　埋他在积雪或三叶草下！

　　他无知无觉，有什么牵挂？

　　　　深深埋下他！

⑤　by：在旁边。

I'LL TELL YOU HOW THE SUN ROSE

I'll tell you how the sun rose—
A ribbon at a time.
The steeples swam in amethyst,
The news like squirrels ran. ①

The hills untied their bonnets,
The bobolinks begun. ②
Then I said softly to myself,
"That must have been the sun!"

But how he set, I know not.
There seemed a purple stile
Which little yellow boys and girls
Were climbing all the while③

Till when they reached the other side,
A dominie in gray④
Put gently up the evening bars,
And led the flock away. ⑤

---

① 本行 = The news ran like squirrels. the news 指太阳升起的消息。

② bobolinks：食米鸟(北美洲一种鸣禽)；begun = began。

③ 本节诗句未完,跨节接 Till....。

我告诉你太阳怎样升起

我告诉你太阳怎样升起：
　　每一次是缎带一条。
教堂的尖塔浮在紫晶中，
　　这消息像松鼠奔跑。

山丘解掉了它们的软帽，
　　波波林克鸟开始唱。
这时我轻轻对我自己说：
　　"那先前肯定是太阳！"

但我不知道它怎样降下。
　　像有个紫色的梯磴，
小小的黄颜色男孩女娃
　　一直在那上面翻登。

等他们翻越到另外一边，
　　一个穿灰衣的教士
在过夜前轻轻上好门闩，
　　然后把小信徒领去。

----

④　dominie：在美国指荷兰改革派教会的牧师，读作['dəumini]，在苏格兰指教师，读作
　　　['dɔmini]。
⑤　flock：一个人管理下的一群人，一个教区的全体教徒，这里指象征夕阳的一群 little
　　　yellow boys and girls。

IT DROPPED SO LOW IN MY REGARD

It dropped so low in my Regard—①

I heard it hit the Ground—②

And go to pieces on the Stones

At bottom of my Mind—

Yet blamed the Fate that fractured—*less*③

Than I reviled Myself,

For entertaining Plated Wares

Upon my Silver Shelf—④

---

① It：无先行词，据下文，指镀银的器皿（所象征的事物）。

② hit the Ground：撞在地面上；美国俚语中也作"坍倒、崩溃"解。

它在我心目里跌到最低

它在我心目里跌到最低——
　　我听见它撞在地面——
撞在我心底里的石板地，
　　就变成了一滩碎片——

要责怪使它跌碎的命运——
　　倒不如把自己咒骂，
因为是我把镀银的器皿
　　捧上了我的银搁架——

---

③　blamed：与上节第 2 行的 heard 并列。the Fate that fractured：fracture 此处是及物
动词，而不表出其宾语，这叫做及物动词的"绝对用法"（absolute use）。

④　这两行意为：因为（我）把镀银的器皿放到摆银器的架子上。

HOPE IS THE THING WITH FEATHERS

Hope is the thing with feathers
That perches in the soul,
And sings the tune without the words,
And never stops at all.

And sweetest in the gale is heard;[①]
And sore must be the storm
That could abash the little bird
That kept so many warm.

I've heard it in the chillest land,
And on the strangest sea;
Yet, never, in extremity,
It asked a crumb of me.

---

① 承上节,本行可理解为 = And the Sweetest tune is heard in the gale, 也可理解为
= And the tune is the sweetest when it is heard in the gale.

希望是个长羽毛的东西

希望是个长羽毛的东西，
　　总是栖伏在灵魂中，
唱的是没有字眼的旋律，
　　而这歌永远不会停。

大风里这歌声听来最美，
　　它暖了多少人的心；
要把这小小的鸟儿吓退，
　　那风暴得实在凶猛。

我曾经在最寒冷的陆地、
　　在最陌生的海上听；
可它从没向我要面包屑，
　　哪怕它自己在绝境。

I TAKE A FLOWER AS I GO

I take a flower as I go

My face to justify,^①

He never saw me in this life^②

I might surprise his eye.

I cross the hall with mingled steps

I silently pass the door.

I look on all this world contains

Just his face—nothing more!

---

① 本行 = To justify my face，显示我脸容的固有的美。

我边走边拿着一支花朵

我边走边拿着一支花朵
　衬托我脸儿的美丽；
他从没看到我这种生活，
　也许乍一见会惊异。

我时快时慢地走过门厅
　悄悄地推门进房间。
我瞧这世界包容的一切，
　而这仅仅是他的脸！

---

② 　本行意为：他从没有看见过我这样地生活着（指拿着花或者佩带着花）。

THE AGED STRANGER

(An Incident of the Civil War)

"I was with Grant"—the stranger said;[1]
Said the farmer, "Say no more,
But rest thee here at my cottage porch,[2]
For thy feet are weary and sore."

"I was with Grant"—the stranger said;
Said the farmer, "Nay, no more.[3]
I prithee sit at my frugal board,[4]
And eat of my humble store.

"How fares my boy,—my soldier boy,
Of the old Ninth Army Corps?
I warrant he bore him gallantly[5]
In the smoke and the battle's roar!"

"I know him not," said the aged man,
"And, as I remarked before,
I was with Grant"—"Nay, nay, I know,"
Said the farmer, "say no more."

---

① Grant: Ulysses Simpson Grant(1822—1885)，美国南北战争中北军主将。早年参加美西战争(1846—1848)，功勋卓著，1861 年南北战争爆发，他应召入伍，在北军中任将军，屡建奇功，备受人民爱戴。

② rest thee = rest thyself = rest yourself.

年老的陌生人

（内战中的一件小事）

"我曾跟着格兰特，"陌生人说；
　　农夫道，"别再说下去；
你的脚准走得又累又疼，
　　请歇在我小屋的门廊里。"

"我曾跟着格兰特，"陌生人说；
　　农夫道，"别再说下去。
请你坐在我俭朴的饭桌前，
　　我粗菜淡饭招待你。

"我那当兵的儿子怎么啦——
　　在那老牌第九军里？
他在硝烟和战斗的杀声中，
　　表现准相当了不起！"

"我可并不认识他，"那老兵说，
　　"正像我刚才说过的，
我曾跟着格兰特"——"知道，
　　知道，"农夫说，"别说了。"

---

③　Nay：[古]否定的语气词。no more：承上节，= say no more.

④　prithee ['pri:ði(:)]：[古]感叹词，由 pray thee 缩合而成，= pray 或 please.

⑤　bore him = bore himself；习语 bear oneself 是"表现，举止"的意思。

"He fell in battle,—I see, alas!
   Thou'dst smooth these tidings o'er.⑥
Nay, speak the truth, whatever it be,
   Though it rend my bosom's core."

"I cannot tell," said the aged man,
   "And should have remarked before,
That I was with Grant,—in Illinois,—
   Three years before the war."⑦

Then the farmer spake him never a word,
   But beat with his fist full sore⑧
That aged man, who had worked for Grant
   Three years before the war.

---

⑥　Thou'dst = Thou wouldst. smooth these tidings o'er：把（坏）消息掩饰过去；
　　smooth over，掩饰，也作"弄平、消除"等解，是习语。tidings，复数形式，作单复数
　　用都有。

　　　　"哎呀，我懂了，他已经阵亡！
　　　　　你是想冲淡这消息。
　　　　不行，任真情如何，你得说——
　　　　　哪怕话扎进我心里。"

　　　　"我可说不上，"那老汉说道，
　　　　　"有句话该说在头里：
　　　　我跟格兰特是在战前三年，
　　　　　那时候在伊利诺伊。"

　　　　对那人农夫再也不说话，
　　　　　却握紧了拳头猛击——
　　　　因为这老汉是战争前三年
　　　　　跟着格兰特做生意。

---

⑦　这两行可参看篇首 Grant 条注，南北战争发生前三年，Grant 在伊利诺伊州当店员
　　时，老人曾和他在一起，老人因为 Grant 是赫赫有名的英雄人物，所以口口声声夸
　　说"我曾跟着格兰特"，引起农夫误会。待到弄清情况；农夫大发脾气，以至饱以老
　　拳。

⑧　beat：过去时，它的宾语是 That aged man；full sore 修饰 beat；full ＝ fully；sore ＝
　　sorely，狠狠地。

NO SONGS IN WINTER①

The sky is gray as gray may be，

There is no bird upon the bough，

There is no leaf on vine or tree.

In the Neponset marshes now②

Willow-stems，rosy in the wind，

Shiver with hidden sense of snow.

So too 'tis winter in my mind，

No light-winged fancy comes and stays：

A season churlish and unkind. ③

Slow creep the hours，slow creep the days，

The black ink crusts upon the pen—

Wait till the bluebirds and the jays

And golden orioles come again！

冬 日 无 歌

灰得不能更灰的一片天，
树枝上连鸟儿都没一只，
藤上和树上叶子没一片。

如今在尼邦塞特沼泽地，
柳树的树干在风中发红，
隐隐的雪意使得它颤栗。

冬日也同样来到我心中，
没有轻灵的幻想来待下：
这冷酷的季节怒气冲冲。

钟点慢慢爬，日子慢慢爬，
黑墨水在笔上渐渐干掉——
等待吧直等到樫鸟、松鸦
和黄黄的金莺再次来到。

---

③　本行中，A season 与前面的 winter 同位，churlish and unkind 是后置定语；也可理
　解为前面省略 It is，= It is a churlish and unkind season。

MEMORY

My mind lets go a thousand things,

Like dates of wars and deaths of kings,

And yet recalls the very hour—

'Twas noon by yonder village tower,[①]

And on the last blue noon in May

The wind came briskly up this way,

Crisping the brook beside the road;

Then, pausing here, set down its load[②]

Of pine-scents, and shook listlessly

Two petals from that wild-rose tree.[③]

---

① tower:钟楼（bell tower 或 clock tower）。

② set:过去时,和下行的 shook 并列,主语都是前面的 The wind。

忆

我的心把上千件事情忘记，

如战争和国王驾崩的日期，

可我却记住了那一个时辰：

据村里的钟楼，是中午时分，

是五月里末了的一次天晴，

中午时吹起了爽人的清风，

吹皱了路边的那一条小溪；

那阵风吹过处，松树香四溢，

而且，从那株野玫瑰的树间，

懒懒地摇下了花瓣儿两片。

③　tree：本诗是用两行一个韵的偶句体写的（每行都含八个音节构成的四音步），这里 tree 和 listlessly 两词不完全押韵，称为"不完全韵的近似韵"，诗中常见。

BY THE PACIFIC OCEAN

Here room and kingly silence keep
Companionship in state austere; ①
The dignity of death is here,
The large, lone vastness of the deep.
Here toil has pitched his camp to rest: ②
The west is banked against the west.

Above yon gleaming skies of gold
One lone imperial peak is seen;
While gathered at his feet in green
Ten thousand foresters are told. ③
And all so still! so still the air ④
That duty drops the web of care.

Beneath the sunset's golden sheaves
The awful deep walks with the deep, ⑤
Where silent sea-doves slip and sweep,
And commerce keeps her loom and weaves. ⑥
The dead red men refuse to rest;
Their ghosts illume my lurid West. ⑦

---

① in state austere = in austere state.
② pitched his camp: 扎营。
③ told: 数。
④ so still the air = so still is the air = the air is so still.

在太平洋之滨

BARNACLES

　　　寥廓和君临一切的寂静
　　　严峻地在这里结成伴侣；
　　　死亡的威严也是在这里，
　　　在这空阔寂寥的海洋中。
　　　辛劳在这里支帐篷安歇，
　　　西部之外依然是西部接。

　　　那边耀金光的天空上面，
　　　只见有巍峨的孤峰一座；
　　　在它葱绿的山脚旁，据说，
　　　聚集有林中的居民一万。
　　　都这么静！空中静成这样，
　　　使职责放下了操心之网。

　　　落日的一束束金辉下方，
　　　庄严的大海与汪洋同行，
　　　那里，掠飞的海鸥不出声，
　　　商业在其织机上织得忙。
　　　已死的红种人不肯长眠，
　　　他们的魂映红了我西天。

---

⑤　本行为"海连海"之意，比较前面第 1 节末行 The west is banked against the west，
　　西面贴着西面，即西面过去还是更远的西面，与"海连海"是同样的形象化写法。

⑥　commerce keeps her loom and weaves：以穿梭织布比喻海上商业（具体是商船）往
　　来。

⑦　末两行因西方血红的夕阳而联想起在西部死去的那些红种人。

BARNACLES[①]

My soul is sailing through the sea,

But the Past is heavy and hindereth me,

The Past hath crusted and cumbrous shells

That hold the flesh of cold sea smells about my soul.

The huge waves wash, the high waves roll,

Each barnacle clingeth and worketh dole [②]

　　And hindereth me from sailing!

Old Past, let go and drop i' the sea[③]

Till fathomless waters cover thee!

For I am living and thou art dead;

Thou drawest back; I strive ahead the day to find. [④]

Thy shells unbind! Night comes behind;[⑤]

I needs must hurry with the wind

　　And trim me best for sailing. [⑥]

---

① Barnacles ['bɑ:nəklz]：藤壶，在本诗中指"过去"对诗人的思想负担。

② worketh dole：引起悲哀；work 作"造成，引起"解时，过去时和过去分词用 wrought。

③ i'＝ in.

④ the day to find＝to find the day.

藤　壶

我的灵魂在穿越着大海，

但沉重的往事把我妨碍；

往事是一种累赘的贝壳，

壳中肉有我灵魂里冷冷海水的气息。

惊涛在翻滚，骇浪在冲击，

紧贴的藤壶却使我悲戚，

　　妨碍着我这船的航行！

早先的往事，掉向海中吧，

直到你压在深深海水下！

因为我活着而你已死亡；

我向前冲去找白天，你却把我妨碍。

你放开！夜已从后面追来，

我得乘这风把速度加快，

　　使自己最适宜于航行。

---

⑤　behind：与行内的 unbind 押韵，是谓"行内韵"。本诗作者是位音乐家，诗作富于音乐
　　美。本诗（尤其是第一节）中头韵及行内韵用得较多，译文对此有所反映。又，按本诗
　　格律，每节第 4、5、6 行押韵，但这里第 6 行 wind 和 behind 是为"眼韵"。

⑥　trim me = trim myself (up).

MARSH SONG—AT SUNSET

Over the monstrous shambling sea,
  Over the Caliban sea,[①]
Bright Ariel-cloud, thou lingerest:
Oh wait, oh wait, in the warm red West,—
  Thy Prospero I'll be.

Over the humped and fishy sea,
  Over the Caliban sea
O cloud in the West, like a thought in the heart
Of pardon, loose thy wing, and start,
  And do a grace for me.

Over the huge and huddling sea,
  Over the Caliban sea,
Bring hither my brother Antonio,—Man,—[②]
My injurer: night breaks the ban:[③]
  Brother, I pardon thee.

---

① Caliban['kælibæn]:卡力班与本诗中的爱丽尔(Ariel['ɛəriəl])、普洛士贝罗(Prospero['prɔspərəu])、安东尼(Antonio[æn'təuniəu])都是莎士比亚剧本《暴风雨》中
  的人物。普洛士贝罗是个公爵,被兄弟安东尼篡夺爵位,放逐到海上,同他女儿栖身
  荒岛上,潜心研究法术。卡力班是个女巫所生的半兽人,在普洛士贝罗管束下,干些
  粗重活儿;爱丽尔则是聪明的精灵,奉普洛士贝罗命,把在海上遇险的邪恶兄弟安
  东尼等人带到他跟前,终于被他感化,把爵位还与普洛士贝罗。

日落时的沼泽之歌

在大得出奇的呆滞的海上，
　在卡力班似的海上，
鲜明的爱丽尔云彩留一留，
等着看我来做普洛士贝罗，
　等在暖又红的西方。

在无精打采的难看的海上，
　在卡力班似的海上，
西天的云啊，像宽容的心思，
请张开你翅膀，倏忽地飞去，
　我要你给我帮个忙。

在巨大而挤挤拥拥的海上，
　在卡力班似的海上，
你把我兄弟安东尼带过来，
他伤害过我，夜把这事抹开——
　兄弟啊，我把你原谅。

---

② Man：呼语，是一种亲热的称呼。

③ My injurer：是上行 my brother Antonio 的同位语。breaks the ban：解除咀咒，解禁。

THE STRONG

Dost deem him weak that owns his strength is tried?[①]

 Nay, we may safely lean on him that grieves:[②]

The pine has immemorially sighed,

 The enduring poplar's are the trembling leaves. [③]

To feel, and bow the head, is not to fear;

 To cheat with jest—that is the coward's art:[④]

Beware the laugh that battles back the tear;[⑤]

 He's false to all that's traitor to his heart. [⑥]

He of great deeds does grope amid the throng[⑦]

 Like him whose steps toward Dagon's temple bore;[⑧]

These's ever something sad about the strong—

 A look, a moan, like that on ocean's shore.

---

① Dost deem him weak...? =Dost thou (Do you) deem him weak...?

② Nay:[古] = No.

③ The enduring poplar's = The enduring poplar's leaves.

④ art:诡计。

⑤ Beware = Beware of,用于祈使句。

强　者

他承认力竭计穷，你算他软弱？
　　不，发喟叹的人却最值得信赖：
松树叹息的年月已难于追溯，
　　叶子在抖的杨树能坚持下来。

有感觉并低下头来，不算害怕；
　　用打趣蒙混却是懦夫的花招：
背叛自己心的人对谁都作假；
　　要警惕硬把眼泪压下的大笑。

就像一个人走向大衮的圣堂，
　　成大事得在人群中摸索前进；
即使强者也总会露出点悲伤——
　　一个眼色或浪拍岸似的呻吟。

---

⑥　本行 = He that is traitor to his heart is false to all.

⑦　He of great deeds = He who does great deeds.

⑧　toward Dagon's [ˈdeigənz] temple bore = bore toward Dagon's temple; bore (bear
的过去时) toward，向……行去；Dagon，大衮，古代非利士(the Philistines)国神，在
腓尼基(Phenicia)受人崇拜，见《圣经·旧约·撒母耳纪上》第 5 章。

LAUGH AND THE WORLD LAUGHS WITH YOU

Laugh and the world laughs with you;[1]
　　Weep, and you weep alone;
For this brave old earth must borrow its mirth,[2]
　　It has trouble enough of its own.
Sing, and the hills will answer;
　　Sigh! it is lost on the air;[3]
The echoes bound to a joyful sound,
　　But shrink from voicing care.[4]

Rejoice, and men will seek you;
　　Grieve, and they turn and go;
They want full measure of all your pleasure,
　　But they do not want your woe.
Be glad, and your friends are many;
　　Be sad, and you lose them all—
There are none to decline your nectared wine,
　　But alone you must drink life's gall.

Feast, and your halls are crowded;
　　Fast, and the world goes by,
Succeed and give, and it helps you live,[5]
　　But no man can help you die.
There is room in the halls of pleasure
　　For a long and lordly train;
But one by one we must all file on[6]
　　Through the narrow aisles of pain.

---

① 本行＝If（或 When）you laugh, the world laughs with you.

② brave old earth：这里的 brave 用的是古义，＝fine, excellent。本诗每节的第3、第7
行都押行内韵（有的是眼韵），译文从之。

你欢笑，人们就同你一起笑

你欢笑，人们就同你一起笑；
　　你悲哭，你就独自哭。
这华美老世界的欢乐只靠借——
　　它自己的麻烦已够多。
你歌唱，山丘把你的歌应和；
　　可叹息呢在风中消失——
回声啊总蹦向快活的声响，
　　但会在哀诉前退却。

你高兴，人们都想来亲近你；
　　你伤心，他们就转身走——
他们所要的是你全部欢乐，
　　他们可不要你的愁。
你愉快，你就有许多的朋友；
　　你悲哀，他们就跑光——
没人不接受你香甜的美酒，
　　可生活的苦汁你独尝。

你设宴，你客厅里挤满宾客；
　　你斋戒，没人来拜访。
你成功又慷慨，日子就欢快；
　　你要死，可没人帮忙。
喜气洋洋的厅堂里，容得下
　　气宇轩昂的长队伍；
但悲悲切切的狭窄侧廊里，
　　我们得一一挨次走。

---

③ it：指前面 Sigh（动词）这个动作，并无具体的先行词。

④ voicing care：出声的忧患，如叹息、哀诉。

⑤ it：指 Succeed 和 give 的境况和行为。

⑥ file on：排成纵队向前走，鱼贯而行。

LITTLE BOY BLUE

The little toy dog is covered with dust,
　　But sturdy and staunch he stands;[①]
The little toy soldier is red with rust,
　　And his musket moulds in his hands.
Time was when the little toy dog was new,[②]
　　And the soldier was passing fair;[③]
And that was the time when our Little Boy Blue
　　Kissed them and put them there.

"Now, don't you go till I come," he said,
　　"And don't you make any noise!"
So, toddling off to his trundle-bed,[④]
　　He dreamt of the pretty toys;
And, as he was dreaming, an angel song
　　Awakened our Little Boy Blue—[⑤]
Oh! the years are many, the years are long,
　　But the little toy friends are true!

Aye, faithful to Little Boy Blue they stand,
　　Each in the same old place—
Awaiting the touch of a little hand,
　　The smile of a little face;
And they wonder, as waiting the long years through
　　In the dust of that little chair,
What has become of our Little Boy Blue,
　　Since he kissed them and put them there.

---

① 本行＝ But he stands sturdy and staunch；这里连用三个 S 起首的词，头韵很响亮。
② Time was when... ＝ There was a time when...，常用于回忆或追述一去不复返
的往事。

蓝 孩 儿

小小的玩具狗身上蒙着灰尘，
　　可照旧雄纠纠傲然肃立；
小小的玩具兵满是红色锈斑，
　　发霉的步枪还握在手里。
小小的玩具狗曾有新的时候，
　　小小的玩具兵也曾漂亮；
那时我们的蓝孩儿吻着它们，
　　把它们安放在这个地方。

他说，"我回来以前你们别走开，
　　也不要发出一点儿声响！"
蹒跚的他走向带轮子的小床，
　　进了满是好玩具的梦乡；
他正在梦乡时，一支天使的歌
　　却把我们的蓝孩儿唤醒——
啊，已这么多年，这么长时间，
　　小小的玩具却忠贞坚定！

是啊，它们真是听蓝孩儿的话，
　　各自站在它们的老地方——
等待一只把它们抚摸的小手，
　　等待一张带笑的小脸庞；
它们在尽是灰尘的小椅子里
　　等了这么久，正在疑惑着：
蓝孩儿吻它们、把它们放下后，
　　这么多年来究竟怎么了？

---

③　passing fair：非常漂亮；passing，[古] 非常地。

④　trundle-bed：有脚轮的矮床，也单称 trundle。

⑤　an angel song/ Awakened our Little Boy Blue：天使的歌唤醒他，即召他上天国（归天）去。

OPPORTUNITY①

In an old city by the storied shores,②

Where the bright summit of Olympus soars,③

A cryptic statue mounted toward the light—

Heel-winged, tip-toed, and poised for instant flight.④

"O statue, tell your name," a traveler cried;

And solemnly the marble lips replied:

"Men call me Opportunity. I lift

My winged feet from earth to show how swift

My flight, how short my stay—⑤

How Fate is ever waiting on the way."

"But why that tossing ringlet on your brow?"

"That men may seize me any moment: *Now*,

Now is my other name; today my date;

O traveler, tomorrow is too late!"

---

① 这是一首基本上用英雄偶句体（每两行一韵，每行是含五音步的十个音节）写成的十四行诗。

② storied：在历史或传奇中传述的。

③ Olympus：（希腊的）奥林匹斯山，也指希腊神话中同名的山，那是诸神居住的地方。

机　会

广为传说的海岸上有座古城，

城后是清朗的奥林匹斯山峰；

城里，神秘的雕像面对那光明——

它踮着生翼的脚像即将飞行。

过路的人问，"你叫什么，雕像啊？"

他大理石的嘴唇庄严地回答：

"人们把我称作是机会，我踮起

长着翅膀的脚是为了要显示：

我逗留之短，飞行之快——

半路上总有命运女神在等待。"

"但你额上怎么有飘动的鬈发？"

"为让人随时可以抓住我：眼下，

我又叫眼下；我只生活在今日；

哦，过路的人哪！明天可太迟！"

---

④　poised for instant flight：摆好立即起飞的姿势。

⑤　My flight：后面省略 is，这行末后的 my stay 后面也省略 is。这一行仅三音步，是为了强调 short。

WORK[①]

Let me but do my work from day to day,[②]
　　In field or forest, at the desk or loom,
　　In roaring market-place or tranquil room;
Let me but find it in my heart to say,[③]
When vagrant wishes beckon me astray,
　　"This is my work; my blessing, not my doom;
　　Of all who live, I am the one by whom
This work can best be done in the right way."

Then shall I see it not too great, nor small,[④]
　　To suit my spirit and to prove my powers;
　　Then shall I cheerful greet the laboring hours,[⑤]
And cheerful turn, when the long shadows fall
　　At eventide, to play and love and rest,[⑥]
　　Because I know for me my work is best.

---

①　这是一首意大利式的十四行诗,其韵式为 abba abba cdd cee。
②　but＝only.
③　it:是后面 to say 的先行词,say 接后面一段直接引语。

工　作

　　我只希望：让我做我每天的工作——

　　　　在田里或在林间，书桌或织机前，

　　　　在喧闹的市场，或在宁静的房间；

　　当闲思逸兴招着手，引诱我中辍，

　　我只希望，我的心里有这话要说：

　　　　"这工作不是厄运，是上天的恩典；

　　　　而这一份工作，在所有的人中间，

　　只有我才能做得最完善和稳妥。"

　　我将会看到，它恰好合我的心愿，

　　　　合我的能力，不太难也不太容易；

　　　　于是我高兴地付出艰苦的努力。

　　等黄昏把长长的影子投向地面，

　　　　我将高兴地去作乐、恋爱和休息，

　　　　因为我知道：对工作我尽了全力。

---

④　shall I see it ＝I shall see it，it 指 my work。

⑤　cheerful＝cheerfully。

⑥　turn...to play and love and rest：这里的 to 可视为介词，把 play，love 和 re
　　三个名词，作介词宾语；也可把这 to 视为动词不定式符号，而把 play，
　　为动词不定式；两种讲法都可以。

SPRING ECSTASY

Oh, let me run and hide,
　Let me run straight to God;
The weather is so mad with white
　From sky down to the clod!

If but one thing were so,
　Lilac, or thorn out there,①
It would not be, indeed,
　So hard to bear.

The weather has gone mad with white;
　The cloud, the highway touch.②
White lilac is enough;
　White thorn too much!

---

① shall I see it = I shall see it. it = my work.
② cheerful; cheerful.
③ noun ... to play; and low ... and rest, 译作 to 用来引出
十六行 ......

与上行 one thing 同位。

销魂的春天

啊，让我跑去藏起来，
　　让我直跑到上帝那里；
天上到地下一片白色，
　　叫天气变得如痴如迷！

倘若外面开着白花的，
　　只是丁香或者山楂树，
说真的，那也就不至于
　　叫人难熬到如此地步。

天气被白花逗得痴迷，
　　再加云和公路的色泽。
单单白丁香就已足够，
　　加上白山楂可就太多！

---

② The cloud，the highway touch：可理解为后面省略 and so on are all white；这里的 touch 是名词，是"润色、色泽"之意。

WASHINGTON

Oh, hero of our younger race!
　　Great builder of a temple new![1]
Ruler, who sought no lordly place!
　　Warrior who sheathed the sword he drew!

Lover of men, who saw afar
　　A world unmarred by want or war,
Who knew the path, and yet forbore
　　To tread, till all men should implore;
Who saw the light, and led the way
　　Where the gray world might greet the day;

Father and leader, prophet sure,[2]
　　Whose will in vast works shall endure,[3]
How shall we praise him on this day of days,[4]
　　Great son of fame who has no need of praise?

How shall we praise him? Open wide the doors
　　Of the fair temple whose broad base he laid.
Through its white halls a shadowy cavalcade
　　Of heroes moves o'er unresounding floors—[5]
Men whose brawned arms upraised these colors high[6]
　　And reared the towers that vanish in the sky,—
The strong who, having wrought, can never, never die.[7]

---

① a temple new = a new temple; temple 比喻 state。

② prophet sure; 确实是先知。

③ 本行= Whose will shall (=will) endure in vast works.

④ this day of days; 指华盛顿的生日, 2 月 22 日。

华 盛 顿

哦,我们年轻民族的英雄
　　　　把崭新的伟大殿堂建立!
他治理国家却不谋尊荣,
　　　　是让出鞘剑入鞘的战士!

他热爱世人,看到的世界
　　　　不因匮乏和战争而残缺;
他知道路径但不急于走,
　　　　直等到大家都把他恳求;
他看到光明,他领头示范,
　　　　要灰色世界能迎接白天。

这国父兼领袖是位先知,
　　　　多少事得贯彻他的意志;
他既是无需赞美地伟大,
　　　　他生日我们怎样赞美他?

我们怎样赞美? 这美好的殿堂
　　　　他奠定宏大基础,要敞开殿门!
在其白色大厅的静悄悄地上
　　　　走过一长列缥缥渺渺的英雄——
他们粗壮的手高举这些旗帜,
　　　　把顶端耸入云间的塔楼竖立——
作出贡献的强者永不被忘记。

---

⑤　a shadowy cavalcade/Of heroes moves o'er unresounding floors:诗人似见建国英雄
　　的英灵无声地移动着。

⑥　brawned:这个词是由名词 brawn (肌肉)加-ed 构成的形容词。

⑦　having wrought:此处没有把宾语表出,这是及物动词的"绝对用法"。

THE NEW MEMORIAL DAY

"Under the roses the blue;

Under the lilies the gray."[1]

Oh, the roses we plucked for the blue,[2]

　And the lilies we twined for the gray,

We have bound in a wreath,

And in silence beneath

　Slumber our heroes today.

Over the new-turned sod

　The sons of our fathers stand,

And the fierce old fight

Slips out of sight

　In the clasp of a brother's hand.[3]

For the old blood left a stain

　That the new has washed away,

And the sons of those

That have faced as foes[4]

　Are marching together today.

---

[1]　蓝军服指南北战争中的北军，灰军服指南军；如美语中常用 blue-coat 指南北战争中的北军。这两行引语的出处不详。

[2]　the roses we plucked＝the roses that（或 which）we plucked；下一行 the lilies we twined 同此；roses 和 lilies 都是第 3 行 have bound 的宾语。

新的阵亡将士纪念日

"玫瑰下面是蓝军服；
百合下面是灰军服。"

哦，为灰军服编的百合，
　　　哦，为蓝军服摘的玫瑰，
我们已扎成个花圈；
我们的英雄在今天
　　　正在寂静的下面沉睡。

新近翻过的这片地上
　　　站着我们先辈的后代.
兄弟们的手一握中，
那往日的酷烈战争
　　　在人们眼中不复存在。

因为前人留下的血渍
　　　已经被后人洗刷干净；
前辈虽然是仇人，
可是他们的子孙
　　　如今却正在并肩前进。

---

③　the clasp of a brother's hand：兄弟握手，谓南北双方原是同胞，今重归于好。
④　faced as foes = faced one another as foes.

Oh, the blood that our fathers gave!

Oh, the tide of our mothers' tears!

And the flow of red,[5]

And the tears they shed,

Embittered a sea of years.[6]

But the roses we plucked for the blue,

And the lilies we twined for the gray,

We have bound in a wreath,

And in glory beneath

Slumber our heroes today.

---

⑤　flow of red：流血。

哦，男祖先流过的鲜血！
　　哦，女先人淌过的眼泪！
这流淌过的泪和血，
使以往的多少岁月
　　成了茫茫一片的伤悲。

但为灰军服编的百合，
　　但为蓝军服摘的玫瑰，
我们已扎成个花圈：
我们的英雄在今天
　　已在下面光荣地安睡。

⑥　a sea of years：茫茫岁月；a sea of：大量，茫茫一片，是习语，如言 a sea of troubles。

A VAGABOND SONG

There is something in the autumn that is native to my
    blood—
Touch of manner, hint of mood;①
And my heart is like a rhyme,
With the yellow and the purple and the crimson keeping
    time.②

The scarlet of the maples can shake me like a cry
Of bugles going by.
And my lonely spirit thrills
To see the frosty asters like a smoke upon the hills.

There is something in October sets the gypsy blood astir;③
We must rise and follow her,④
When from every hill of flame⑤
She calls and calls each vagabond by name.⑥

---

① 本行是上行 something 的同位语；a touch of 和 a hint of 作"一些儿、些微"解，在诗
    歌中省略冠词"a"。mood 与上行的 blood 押"眼韵"。
② keeping time：(秋色随时间而变化) 形成节奏，合拍。
③ 本行中 sets 前面省略代替 something 的关系代词 that；astir 是宾语补足语，gypsy
    blood 和 astir 之间存在逻辑上的主谓关系，因而 gypsy blood astir 构成 sets 的复合
    宾语。

漫游者的歌

秋天里含着一种我血液中天生的东西——
有那点习性，带那缕情绪；
我的心有如押韵的诗一首，
合着黄的节奏、紫的节奏和深红的节奏。

一株株枫树的殷红能够使我周身震颤——
像飘过一声军号的召唤。
我孤寂的心灵一阵颤抖——
当我看到带霜的翠菊像烟弥漫在山丘。

十月里，有着使吉普赛血液骚动的东西；
从火焰般的一座座山里，
当她一遍又一遍地呼唤
每个漂泊者名字，我们得起身把她追赶。

---

④ her：指上行的 something。

⑤ hill of flame：枫叶如火一般红遍满山，故称"火焰般的山"。

⑥ calls and calls：连用两个 calls，如闻反复的呼唤在山岭间回响不止。

THE SEA GYPSY

I am fevered with the sunset,

I am fretful with the bay,

For the wander-thirst is on me[1]

And my soul is in Cathay.[2]

There's a schooner in the offing,[3]

With her topsails shot with fire,[4]

And my heart has gone aboard her

For the Islands of Desire.

I must forth again to-morrow![5]

With the sunset I must be

Hull down on the trail of rapture[6]

In the wonder of the sea.

---

① wander-thirst：＝wander fever，都是"漫游热"的意思。

② Cathay：[古、诗]中国。而古代印度等地的人称中国为震旦。

③ in the offing：在看得到的远处海面上。

④ shot with fire：闪着(如)火(的)光；这里的 shot 是形容词，作"闪光的"解。

海上吉卜赛

我兴奋激动是为了日落，
　　我焦躁是为了海湾，
因为我渴望去漂泊漫游，
　　我的魂已去了震旦。

远远的海面有条双桅船，
　　中桅帆火一般闪亮，
我的心早已经登上了它，
　　要驶向那愿望之乡。

我明天一定要再度出发！
　　一定得驶进夕阳里，
沿欢乐的海路孤帆远去，
　　溶进那大海的神奇。

---

⑤　本行＝I must set forth again to-morrow! 类似句型参见莎士比亚剧本 *Timon of Athens* 第四幕一场，35 行 "Timon will to the woods" ＝Timon will go to the woods.

⑥　Hull down：(船只)远在只见桅杆，看不到船身的地方，是习语，作修饰词用。

COMRADES

Comrades, pour the wine tonight,
　For the parting is with dawn. [①]
Oh, the clink of cups together,
　With the daylight coming on!
　　Greet the morn
　　With a double horn,
When strong men drink together!

Comrades, gird your swords tonight,
　For the battle is with dawn.
Oh, the clash of shields together,
　With the triumph coming on!
　　Greet the foe
　　And lay him low, [②]
When strong men fight together.

Comrades, watch the tides tonight,
　For the sailing is with dawn.
Oh, to face the spray together, [③]
　With the tempest coming on!
　　Greet the Sea
　　With a shout of glee,
When strong men roam together.

---

① with dawn：随着黎明的到来。
② lay him low：把他打倒在地上，打败他。

战 友 们

今夜来痛饮一番，战友们，
　　因为分手就在拂晓。
啊，酒杯丁当地碰在一起——
　　一片曙光正在来到！
　　　去迎接侵早，
　　　吹起双管的号角——
当坚强的人们痛饮在一起！

今夜你们佩上剑，战友们，
　　因为决战就在拂晓。
啊，盾牌铿锵地撞在一起——
　　一次胜利正在来到！
　　　去迎战顽敌，
　　　把他们杀翻在地——
当坚强的人们战斗在一起。

今夜要注意潮水，战友们，
　　因为出航就在拂晓。
啊，冲向浪花时全在一起——
　　一场暴风雨在来到！
　　　去迎向海洋，
　　　发出欢乐的叫嚷——
当坚强的人们航行在一起。

---

③　Oh, to face the spray together = Oh, let's face...：这是不定式动词的一种特殊用法。

Compades, give a cheer tonight,④
  For the dying is with dawn.
Oh, to meet the stars together,⑤
  With the silence coming on!
    Greet the end
    As a friend a friend,⑥
When strong men die together.

④　give a cheer：参考习语 give three cheers。
⑤　stars：占星术中所谓的"司命星"，常用复数，转义为"命运"。

今夜同声欢呼吧，战友们，
　　因为拼死就在拂晓。
啊，面对命运时全在一起——
　　一片寂静正在来到！
　　迎接这结局，
　　　像朋友把朋友迎接——
当坚强的人们牺牲在一起。

---

⑥　As a friend a friend：承上行，= As a friend greets a friend.

ON A SOLDIER FALLEN IN THE PHILIPPINES[①]

Streets of the roaring town,
Hush for him; hush, be still!
He comes, who was stricken down
Doing the word of our will.
Hush! Let him have his state,[②]
Give him his soldier's crown,
The grists of trade can wait
Their grinding at the mill,
But he cannot wait for his honor, now the trumpet
has been blown,
Wreathe pride now for his granite brow, lay love
on his breast of stone.

Toll! Let the great bells toll
Till the clashing air is dim.
Did we wrong this parted soul?
We will make it up to him.[③]
Toll! Let him never guess
What work we sent him to.
Laurel, laurel, yes;
He did what we bade him do.
Praise, and never a whispered hint but the fight
he fought was good;[④]
Never a word that the blood on his sword was his
country's own heart's-blood.[⑤]

---

① 本诗发表于 1901 年,也即在发生美菲战争之际。

② have his state：享有他应得的尊严（隆重礼遇,此处指哀荣）。

③ make it up to him：弥补,补偿,是口语中常用的习语,其中的 it 无所专指。

为倒下在菲律宾的一名士兵而作

别出声，请为他安静，
这城里的喧闹街道！
他来了，就为了执行
我们的旨意被撂倒。
别出声，就让他光彩，
给他以战士的花冠。

百行百业能待一待，
不忙推生利的磨盘，
可是他却不能够把自己的荣誉等候，
眼下喇叭都已吹响；
为他山岩般面容编光荣的花环，把爱
洒在他石头般胸膛。

敲吧！把丧钟敲起来，
敲到铿锵的天空暗。
我们把这离魂亏待？
我们要补偿这一点。
敲吧！敲得他猜不到
我们曾派他什么活。
桂冠，桂冠，错不了；
派他干的活他已做。
赞扬他，只能说他打的那一仗相当好，
其他的千万别吭声；
至于他剑上的血是他祖国的心头血——
这事万不能露口风。

---

④ never a whispered hint but... = never give（或 drop, let fall）a whispered hint except.

⑤ 要人们只字不提他刀上的血乃是他祖国心上的血，这含有深刻的讽刺意义。

A flag for the soldier's bier
Who dies that his land may live;[6]
O, banners, banners here,
That he doubt not nor misgive!
That he heed not from the tomb
The evil days draw near
When the nation, robed in gloom,
With its faithless past shall strive;[7]
Let him never dream that his bullet's scream went
    wide of its island mark,[8]
Home to the heart of his darling land where she
    stumbled and sinned in the dark.[9]

---

[6] that＝so that.

[7] 本行＝ shall strive with its faithless past; strive with 与 strive against 同义,都是
"与……作斗争"的意思。

[8] went wide of：偏离(目标)很远。

[9] Home to：承上行,＝went home to,打中。she 指美国。

他为祖国的生而死——
　为他的灵柩盖上旗；
这儿呀，旗帜、旗帜，
　免得他多虑和怀疑！
让他在墓中想不到
　不祥的日子已接近——
他国家被阴云笼罩，
　挣扎在往日不义中。
让他永远也梦想不到：他呼啸的子弹
　远离了这岛国鸽的——
当他亲爱的祖国在黑暗中失足造孽，
　射向了她那心脏里。

本诗发表于 1901 年。在 1898 年 4 月至 12 月的西美战争中，美国军队一方面在古巴对西作战，另一方面向当时是西班牙属地的菲律宾群岛进攻。在马尼拉湾战役中，于 5 月 1 日占领了马尼拉城。西班牙战败后，在放弃古巴、将关岛和波多黎各割让美国的同时，以 2000 万美元的代价把菲律宾群岛的主权转让美国。此后，美国占领军被用来攻击一些菲律宾的地方武装，以镇压菲律宾人民为争取民族独立而进行的斗争。

WHEN UNDER THE ICY EAVES

When under the icy eaves

　　The swallow heralds the sun,

And the dove for its lost mate grieves,

　　And the young lambs play and run;

When the sea is a plain of grass,

　　And the blustering winds are still,

And the strength of the thin snows pass

　　In the mists o'er the tawny hill——

The spirit of life awakes[①]

In the fresh flags by the lakes.

---

① The spirit of life awakes: 生机复苏。全诗只短短十行,从檐下到田间,从海上到山上,最后回到湖滨几枝新菖蒲,好一片静谧而又生气盎然的早春景色。

当结冰的檐下燕子来

当结冰的檐下燕子来，
　　把阳光的消息先预告；
当鸽子为丧偶而悲哀，
　　当小羔羊玩耍又奔跑；
当海面像一片大草原，
　　当怒吼的狂风已停止，
当残雪在赭色的山间
　　在雾气下无力地消失——
瞧湖畔苗壮的新菖蒲，
知万物的生机已复苏。

AN OLD STORY[①]

Strange that I did not know him then,[②]

　　That friend of mine!

I did not even show him then

　　One friendly sign;

But cursed him for the ways he had

　　To make me see[③]

My envy of the praise he had

　　For praising me.[④]

I would have rid the earth of him

　　Once, in my pride....

I never knew the worth of him

　　Until he died.

---

① 本诗中所有的奇数行都押三重韵(triple rhyme) 这种韵式都用于幽默诗、讽刺诗;
　译文只押了两字韵。

② Strange that ＝ It is strange that.

③ To make me see:这个不定式短语修饰上行的 ways。

一个老故事

奇怪，我那时竟不了解他，

　　不了解那朋友！

连友好的表示也没给他，

　　竟一次也没有；

反倒诅咒他，因为他让我

　　看到我妒忌他——

他获得赞扬就凭赞扬我——

　　他真会说好话。

有一回我的自尊差一点

　　使得他离尘世……

在他去世前我从来一点

　　不知道他价值。

---

④　the praise he had /For praising me：他因赞扬我而自己得到的赞扬。这个词组从字面讲，也可理解为"他赞扬我时所用的赞扬的话"。这样的话，译文可作"妒忌他自有词儿赞扬我"。

THE DARK HILLS

Dark hills at evening in the west,

Where sunset hovers like a sound

Of golden horns that sang to rest①

Old bones of warriors under ground,

Far now from all the bannered ways

Where flash the legions of the sun,②

You fade—as if the last of days

Were fading and all wars were done. ③

---

① rest：这里是及物动词，作"使休息、使安息"解。

② legions：原指古罗马的军团，今指一般军团，转而也作"众多"解。本诗中用 horns，warriors，bannered ways，legions 等一系列与古代战争有关的词，使人联想起千古争战不息。

幽暗的山丘

傍晚时西面幽暗的山丘！

落日在你那里盘桓低徊，

像黄金号角的齐声吹奏

叫地下的武士骸骨安睡；

你现在离旌旗之路已远——

那路上闪烁着阳光军团——

你在隐没，像最后的白天

在隐没，而仗已全部打完。

---

③ 本诗全诗只是一个句子，而 dark hills 不仅是一视觉意象而且也是一感情上的象征。

WAR IS KIND[1]

Do not weep, maiden, for war is kind.
Because your lover threw wild hands toward the sky
And the affrighted steed ran on alone,
Do not weep.
War is kind.

    Hoarse, booming drums of the regiment,
    Little souls who thirst for fight,[2]
    These men were born to drill and die.
    The unexplained glory flies above them,
    Great is the battle god, great, and his kingdom—
    A field where a thousand corpses lie. [3]
    Do not weep.
    War is kind.

Do not weep, babe, for war is kind.
Because your father tumbled in the yellow trenches,
Raged at his breast, gulped and died,
Do not weep.
War is kind.

    Swift blazing flag of the regiment,
    Eagle with crest of red and gold,[4]
    These men were born to drill and die,
    Point for them the virtue of slaughter,
    Make plain to them the excellence of killing
    And a field where a thousand corpses lie.

Mother whose heart hung humble as a button
On the bright splendid shroud of your son,
Do not weep.
War is kind.

---

[1]   这首讽刺诗写的是一幕幕惨不忍睹的战争景象，却不断重复着"战争很仁慈"。
[2]   Little souls：年轻人。

战争很仁慈

你别哭，姑娘，因为战争很仁慈。
你的情人双手朝着苍天乱挥，
受惊的战马独个儿跑开，
你别哭。
战争很仁慈。

　　响着刺耳嘭嘭声的团队战鼓，
　　渴望战斗的一个个年轻心灵，
　　这些人哪，生来就是得操练和死亡，
　　莫名其妙的荣誉在他们头上飞翔，
　　伟大呀，战神！伟大呀，战神的王国！
　　那是一片躺着万千尸体的土地。
　　你别哭。
　　战争很仁慈。

你别哭，孩子，战争很仁慈。
你爸爸跌进了黄土的壕沟，
对自己的胸膛发火，然后喘着气死掉，
你别哭。
战争很仁慈。

　　着了火、在很快烧掉的军旗啊，
　　带着红色、金黄色冠毛的雄鹰啊，
　　这些人生来就是得操练和死亡。
　　给他们说明大屠杀的妙处吧，
　　给他们指出杀戮，
　　指出躺着万千尸体的战场的美妙吧。

母亲啊，你的心像颗不足道的纽扣，
挂在你儿子光辉灿烂的裹尸布上，
你别哭。
战争很仁慈。

③　A field：与上行的 his kingdom 同位。
④　Eagle with crest of red and gold：指军旗上的雄鹰。

PROMISE

I grew a rose within a garden fair,[①]

And, tending it with more than loving care,

I thought how, with the glory of its bloom,

I should the darkness of my life illume;[②]

And, watching, ever smiled to see the lusty bud

Drink freely in the summer sun to tinct its blood.

My rose began to open, and its hue

Was sweet to me as to it sun and dew;[③]

I watched it taking on its ruddy flame

Until the day of perfect blooming came,

Then hasted I with smiles to find it blushing red—[④]

Too late! Some thoughtless child had plucked my rose and

    fled![⑤]

---

①   a garden fair = a fair garden.

②   the darkness of my life illume＝illume the darkness of my life; illume, [诗]＝illu-

    minate.

期　望

我把玫瑰种在美好的花园里，

以不仅是爱的关怀把它护理；

我以为凭它日后花朵的灿烂，

我将会照亮我生活中的黑暗；

我时时观察，笑看着茁壮的蓓蕾一朵

自在地啜饮夏日的阳光，增添着血色。

花蕾在开放，对于我它的色彩

像露和阳光对于它一样可爱；

我眼看它一天一天变得火红，

直到它完全开足的那天降临；

这时，我赶去看它的赧颜，脸上带着笑——

太迟啦！有个自私孩子已摘了花逃掉！

---

③　as to it sun and dew＝as sun and dew were（或 are）to it；it 指 my rose。

④　hasted I ＝ I hasted.

⑤　thoughtless：这里作"不考虑他人的，自私的"解。

FOREVER

I had not known before
   Forever was so long a word. [1]
The slow stroke of the clock of time
   I had not heard.

'Tis hard to learn so late;
   It seems no sad heart really learns,
But hopes and trusts and doubts and fears,
   And bleeds and burns.

The night is not all dark,
   Nor is the day all it seems,
But each may bring me this relief—
   My dreams and dreams. [2]

I had not known before
   That Never was so sad a word,
So wrap me in forgetfulness—
   I have not heard. [3]

---

[1]　本行和末节的 Never was so sad a word 两句话都是从英谚"Never is a long word"
衍化而来；这个英谚是"不要轻易讲'决不'"的意思，指不要轻易放弃、绝望或作否
定的预测。

永　远

我以前从来不知道
　　"永远"这个词是这个长短。
时光的钟锤缓缓的敲打
　　我不曾听见。

学得这么晚是困难；
　　看来忧愁的心真学不好，
只会希望、信赖、怀疑、恐惧、
　　悲咽和焦躁。

夜并不是完全漆黑，
　　昼不全是它看来的情形，
但昼夜都能给我这解脱：
　　我的梦呀梦。

我以前从来不知道
　　"永远不"这个词这样悲惨，
所以请把我裹进遗忘里——
　　我不曾听见。

---

② My dreams and dreams：叠用 dreams 表示不断的梦想。

③ I have not heard：我没有听到"永远不"，意谓他相信他的梦想不会永远不得实现。

THE DEBT

This is the debt I pay
Just for one riotous day,
Years of regret and grief,
Sorrow without relief.

Pay it I will to the end—①
Until the grave, my friend,②
Gives me a true release—③
Gives me the clasp of peace. ④

Slight was the thing I bought,
Small was the debt I thought,
Poor was the loan at best—
God! but the interest!⑤

---

① 本行= I will pay it to the end；我将还债还到死。

② my friend 是 the grave 的同位语。

③ a true release：一份真正的豁免文书，真正的解脱。

债

只为我一天的胡来，
如今就得还这笔债：
连年的懊恼和悔恨，
悲哀就从此伴一生。

我将会还债还到底——
要到进坟墓的怀里
我这债真正才还清——
那时候我才能安宁。

换来的东西不足道，
原以为代价非常小——
最好的借贷也很差，
上帝呀，利息这么大！

---

④　the clasp of peace：（死的）安宁的怀抱。
⑤　这两行意为：再好的借贷也是可怜的，而利息却不得了（如这里所说，一世都还不了）。

NIGHT CLOUDS

The white mares of the moon rush along the sky[1]

Beating their golden hoofs upon the glass Heavens;[2]

The white mares of the moon are all standing on their hind

    legs.

Pawing at the green porcelain doors of the remote Heavens.

Fly, mares!

Strain your utmost,

Scatter the milky dust of stars,

Or the tiger sun will leap upon you and destroy you

With one lick of his vermilion tongue.

---

[1] The white mares of the moon：以白马比喻月光照耀下奔驰的云；这是典型的意象
派表现手法；请注意全诗形象生动具体、色彩鲜明强烈的特点。

夜　云

月亮的那群白牝马在空中奔驰，

它们的金蹄敲击着玻璃的天庭；

月亮的那群白牝马全都直立而起，

用前蹄叩着遥远天庭的绿瓷门。

飞跑吧，牝马们！

使尽你们的全力，

扬起那银河里乳白色的星斗之尘。

要不，太阳这猛虎会扑向你们，

用它血红的舌头一舔便把你们全消灭。

---

② glass Heavens：玻璃天，和后面第 8 行 tiger sun（老虎太阳）同样是奇特的形象化的
构想，奇特的搭配。

THE SILKEN TENT[①]

She is as in a field a silken tent[②]
At midday when a sunny summer breeze
Has dried the dew and all its ropes relent,
So that in guys it gently sways at ease,[③]
And its supporting central cedar pole,[④]
That is its pinnacle to heavenward[⑤]
And signifies the sureness of the soul,
Seems to owe naught to any single cord,[⑥]
But strictly held by none, is loosely bound[⑦]
By countless silken ties of love and thought
To everything on earth the compass round,[⑧]
And only by one's going slightly taut[⑨]
In the capriciousness of summer air
Is of the slightest bondage made aware.[⑩]

---

① 这是一首严谨的莎士比亚式十四行诗,全诗只一个句子,主句是开首的 She is as in a field a silken tent at midday,余皆修饰部分。

② 本行=She is as a silken tent in a field.

③ 本行=So that it gently sways in guys at ease; it 指 silken tent; guys,支索,牵索。

④ pole:接隔开两行的后面的 Seems,中间插入的两行"That is its pinnacle...of the soul"可理解为放在括弧或破折号中间的插入语,也可把 That 看作相当于 Which,引入一个定语从句,修饰 pole。

⑤ to heavenward = toward heaven.

绸　帐　篷

她像田野之中的一顶绸帐篷，
夏日的微风已把它露水吹干，
正午时它的绳索都不再紧绷，
所以悠悠轻摇在几根牵索间，
而它中央那根雪松木的支柱——
我是说，它那尖顶儿直指穹苍，
表明了里里外外的坚定稳固——
就像不依赖于任何绳索一样；
虽说没一根拉紧它，却有多少
爱和思念的丝结松松地把它
同世界上的万物联结在一道，
只有当夏日微风的任性变化
使某根绳儿微微地绷紧一些，
那种轻巧的束缚才使它察觉。

---

⑥　Seems：它的主语是两行前的 pole，见注 4。

⑦　strictly held by none：过去分词短语，修饰 is bound。

⑧　To everything：承接前面的 is loosely bound。on earth the compass round＝all the world over。

⑨　one's：这里的 one 指 one of the countless ties of love and thought（思念、关心）。

⑩　本行＝Is made aware of the slightest bondage；Is 的主语仍是第 5 行的 pole，与 Seems 和 is bound 并列。

FIRE AND ICE

Some say the world will end in fire,

Some say in ice. [1]

From what I've tasted of desire

I hold with those who favor fire. [2]

But if it had to perish twice, [3]

I think I know enough of hate

To say that for destruction ice

Is also great

And would suffice.

---

① in ice：承上行，＝the world will end in ice.

② hold with：赞同，是习语。

火 与 冰

有人说，毁灭世界的将是火；

有人说，将是冰。

就因为欲望的滋味我尝过，

我认为，说是火的人没说错。

但我想我对恨了解相当深，

所以倘世界得毁灭掉两趟，

我敢说，要世界消灭个干净

冰同样有力量，

而且也肯定行。

---

③　if it had to perish：这里的 had 是虚拟语气，与末行的主句中的 would suffice 呼应。

THE ROSE FAMILY

The rose is a rose,[①]

And was always a rose.

But the theory now goes

That the apple's a rose,

And the pear is, and so's

The plum, I suppose.

The dear only knows[②]

What will next prove a rose.

You, of course, are a rose—

But were always a rose.[③]

---

① rose 既可解释为玫瑰或蔷薇,也可解释为蔷薇科蔷薇属植物(有 100 来种)。诗人在
这里是利用一词多义及植物分类学来称颂自己的妻子。

蔷 薇 科

玫瑰花属于蔷薇科，

在过去这一直是的。

但现在有种理论了，

说苹果也属蔷薇科，

梨树也是的，我捉摸

连李树也属蔷薇科。

天晓得下回是什么

被证明属于蔷薇科。

你当然属于蔷薇科——

不过你一向就是的。

---

② 这一行意为：只有天知道。

③ 本诗中一韵到底，这在英美诗歌中并不多见。

MNEMOSYNE①

It's autumn in the country I remember.

How warm a wind blew here about the ways!

And shadows on the hillside lay to slumber

During the long sun-sweetened summer-days. ②

It's cold abroad the country I remember. ③

The swallows veering skimmed the golden grain④

At midday with wing aslant and limber；

And yellow cattle browsed upon the plain.

It's empty down the country I remember.

I had a sister lovely in my sight：⑤

Her hair was dark, her eyes were very sombre；

We sang together in the woods at night.

----

① Mnemosyne[mni(ː)'mɔzini, niː'mɔsini]：(希腊神话）记忆女神。本诗的韵式较特
殊，值得注意。

② sun-sweetened：因日晒而甜香的。

摩涅莫绪涅

我念中的乡土现在已是秋季。

悠长的夏日里阳光多么甜美，

那时影子都躺在山坡上休憩，

多么暖的风曾在这些路上吹！

我念中的乡土现在一片寒意。

当初燕子后掠的翅膀多轻盈——

午间翻飞着掠过金色的谷粒；

平野上是在吃草的黄黄牛群。

我念中的乡土现在多么清凄。

我眼中曾有一位可爱的姑娘，

她头发乌黑，她眼神深沉忧郁；

夜晚我们曾在树林里一起唱。

---

③　本行意谓：It's cold abroad——in the country (that) I remember.

④　veering：改变着方向，方向不定。

⑤　sister：此词除指"姐妹"外，也指相当于姐妹的女子。

It's lonely in the country I remember.

The babble of our children fills my ears,
And on our hearth I stare the perished ember
To flames that show all starry thro' my tears. [⑥]

It's dark about the country I remember.

There are the mountains where I lived. The path
Is slushed with cattle-tracks and fallen timber,
The stumps are twisted by the tempests' wrath.

But that I knew these places are my own, [⑦]
I'd ask how came such wretchedness to cumber
The earth, and I to people it alone. [⑧]

It rains across the country I remember.

---

⑥ stare the perished ember /To flames：看着死灰复燃（烧起熊熊的火焰）起来。show
all starry thro'[through] my tears：使一切在我泪眼里都显得熠熠闪光；starry 是宾
语补足语，与宾语 all 构成复合宾语。

我念中的乡土现在多么枯寂。

我们孩子的儿语充满我耳中，
壁炉前我朝烧完的灰烬凝视，
透过泪花只见点点的火熊熊。

我念中的乡土现在夜色凄迷。

那儿有我住过的山区；牛的脚、
倒下的树使小径上泥泞满地，
暴风雨肆虐使残株互相缠绕。

要不是我知道这是我的故土，
我会问怎么竟有这样的悲凄
来作践大地，而我在其上独住。

我念中的乡土现在满天雨滴。

---

⑦　But that... ：要不是……

⑧　这两行＝I would ask how such wretchedness came to cumber the earth, and how I came to people it alone.

UNDER THE HARVEST MOON①

Under the harvest moon,

When the soft silver

Drips shimmering②

Over the garden nights,

Death, the gray mocker

Comes and whispers to you

As a beautiful friend

Who remembers.

Under the summer roses,

When the fragrant crimson

Lurks in the dusk

Of the wild red leaves,

Love, with little hands,

Comes and touches you

With a thousand memories,

And asks you

Beautiful unanswerable questions.

---

① Harvest Moon：指秋分（9月22日或9月23日）后两周内的第一次满月，天文学上
称"获月"。

在那获月的下面

在那获月的下面，
当柔和的白银
微微发着亮
滴落在花园的夜色上，
死神这灰色嘲弄者
来对你切切低语，
像记着往事的
一个美丽朋友。

在夏日的玫瑰下面，
当那芬芳的殷红
在热狂红瓣的
阴影中潜伏，
有着小小双手的爱神
来用一千缕的回忆
撩动你，
并问你许多
没法回答的美丽问题。

---

② shimmering：分词，修饰 Drips。

TEN DEFINITIONS OF POETRY

1 Poetry is a projection across silence of cadences arranged[①] to break that silence with definite intentions of echoes, syllables, wave lengths.

2 Poetry is the journal of a sea animal living on land, wanting to fly the air.

3 Poetry is a series of explanations of life, fading off into horizons too swift for explanations.[②]

4 Poetry is a search for syllables to shoot at the barriers of the unknown and the unknowable.

5 Poetry is a theorem of a yellow-silk handkerchief knotted with riddles, sealed in a balloon tied to the tail of a kite flying in a white wind against a blue sky in spring.[③]

6 Poetry is the silence and speech between a wet struggling root of a flower and a sunlit blossom of that flower.

7 Poetry is the harnessing of the paradox of earth cradling life and then entombing it.

8 Poetry is a phantom script telling how rainbows are made and why they go away.[④]

9 Poetry is the synthesis of hyacinths and biscuits.[⑤]

10 Poetry is the opening and closing of a door, leaving those who look through to guess about what is seen during a moment.

---

① a projection across silence of cadences ＝a projection of cadences across silence；倒装的目的是使 cadences 和后面修饰它的过去分词 arranged 紧接在一起。

② swift＝swiftly.

诗的十条定义

1　诗就是穿过寂静的一种音律投射，这音律的安排有明确的目的，要以反响、音节、波长打破那寂静。

2　诗就是一种海洋动物的日记，这动物生活在陆地上，却想在天空翱翔。

3　诗就是对于生活的一连串解释，但这生活过快地隐没在视野之外，快得难以作出解释。

4　诗就是寻找一些合适的音节，用来射向由未知和不可知构成的障碍。

5　诗就是一种原理，这原理是一方真丝的黄手帕，这手帕同谜结扎在一起，封在一个气球里，系在一只风筝的尾部，飞翔在蓝天白云的春风里。

6　诗就是无声和有声的对话，对话的双方是一株花儿奋斗不息的潮湿的根和开放在阳光下的这株花的花朵。

7　诗就是给大地的矛盾套上笼头，这大地既是生命的摇篮，可随后却把生命埋葬。

8　诗就是一种似有似无的天书，说明彩虹如何造成，又为什么消失。

9　诗就是风信子同热松饼的合成物。

10　诗就是门扉的一开一关，让那些打门洞朝另一头看的人们心下嘀咕：在那开和关之间的一刹那，究竟看到了什么。

---

③　theorem：一般原理，公理，后面连用四个分词作不同层次的定语短语，在正常文字中似嫌累赘，在这里正好象征诗的原理的复杂性。

④　phantom script：字面意义为"虚幻的文书"。

⑤　biscuits：在美国指松饼，软饼，在英国指饼干(在美国称饼干为cracker)。

JAZZ FANTASIA

Drum on your drums, batter on your banjoes, sob on the long cool winding saxophones. Go to it, O jazzmen. ①

Sling your knuckles on the bottoms of the happy tin pans, ② let your trombones ooze, and go husha-husha-hush with the slippery sandpaper.

Moan like an autumn wind high in the lonesome treetops, moan soft like you wanted somebody terrible, cry like a③ racing car slipping away from a motorcycle-cop, bang-bang! you jazzmen, bang altogether drums, traps, banjoes, horns, tin cans-make two people fight on the top of a stairway and scratch each other's eyes in a clinch tumbling down the stairs.

Can the rough stuff... now a Mississippi steamboat pushes up④ the night river with a hoo-hoo-hoo-oo... and the green lanterns calling to the high soft stars.... a red moon rides on the humps of the low river hills.... Go to it, O jazzmen.

---

① 这里连用 d,b 和 s 开首的词,都是头韵,拟声效果显著,读来如闻一片热闹的歌声、琴声、萨克管声。Go to it：加油干,干起来,是习语。

② tin pans：白铁罐(作为乐器),他本作 timpans,则指的是定音鼓(kettledrum,一般作 timpani)。

爵士幻想曲

在你们的鼓上咚咚捶吧,在你们的班卓琴上嘣嘣打吧,在
　　弯弯的、凉凉的长长萨克管上抽抽搭搭吧。
　　加油干哪,爵士乐手们。

把你们的指关节朝快活的白铁罐的底上甩,让你们的拉管
　　慢慢悠悠地憋出声来,配着那滑溜溜的砂纸,呼
　　嚓、呼嚓、呼哧地奏起来。

呜呜咽咽吧,像秋风吹在凄凉的高高树顶上;柔声细气地
　　呜咽吧,就像你们渴求着某个妙人儿;呼叫吧,像
　　一辆赛车从驾着摩托车的警察身旁溜走,嘟嘟地
　　奏起来!你们这些爵士乐手,把鼓儿和打击乐器,
　　把喇叭和班卓琴,把白铁罐一起嘟嘟地吹打起来
　　——像两个人在楼梯口打架,让他们扭作一团,
　　滚下楼梯时还抠彼此的眼珠。

这种粗野的东西能不能……现在一艘汽船在密西西比河
　　的夜色里呜呜呜呜地逆流而上……还有一盏盏
　　绿色的提灯呼唤着发出柔光的高天星斗……一
　　轮红红的月亮骑在河边丘陵的低低峰峦上。……
　　加油干吧,爵士乐手们。

---

③　like you wanted＝as if you wanted, 是虚拟语气。altogether,严格地说这里应用 all
　　together。
④　Can the rough stuff...;意谓这种粗野的东西能怎样,由你去想象、领略。

NOVEMBER NIGHT

Listen...
With faint dry sound,[1]
Like steps of passing ghosts,
The leaves, frost-crisp'd, break from the trees[2]
And fall.[3]

NIAGARA[4]

(Seen on a Night in November)

How frail
Above the bulk
Of crashing water hangs,
Autumnal, evanescent, wan,
The moon.[5]

---

① With faint dry soumd：修饰后面的 break。

② frost-crisp'd：霜冻面发脆的。

③ 这种五行诗格律为该女诗人独创（可参看"作者简介"）。

十一月之夜

听啊……
蜷脆霜叶
宛如游魂脚步，
带着枯声悄然离树
而下。

尼亚加拉

（十一月某夜所见）

秋月
挂在浩荡
奔溅水流之上
轻悠纤细而又苍白，
多弱。

---

④　Niagara[nai'æɡərə]：尼亚加拉瀑布(Niagara Falls)。

⑤　The moon：是主语；全句的正常词序是：How frail the autumnal, evanescent, wan
moon hangs above the bulk of crashing water.

FACTORY WINDOWS ARE ALWAYS BROKEN

Factory windows are always broken.
Somebody's always throwing bricks,
Somebody's always heaving cinders,[①]
Playing ugly Yahoo tricks.[②]

Factory windows are always broken.
Other windows are let alone.
No one throws through the chapel-window
The bitter, snarling derisive stone.

Factory windows are always broken.
Something or other is going wrong.
Something is rotten—I think, in Denmark.[③]
End of the factory-window song.

---

① heaving：[口] 扔，掷。
② Yahoo [jə'hu：或 jɑ：'hu：] tricks：Yahoo 原是《格列弗游记》中的人形兽，转指人面兽心的人，在美国俚语中还指粗汉；trick：恶作剧，美国俚语中也作"犯罪行为"解。

工厂的窗子总是被打破

工厂的窗子总是被打破。
有人总是在丢石头扔砖，
有人总是在猛掷着煤渣；
搞些恶作剧，存心乱捣蛋。

工厂的窗子总是被打破。
别处的窗户倒不受破坏。
恶狠狠呼啸的挑衅石头，
没人朝教堂的窗子砸来。

工厂的窗子总是被打破。
反正有什么地方出了岔，
出了大毛病（我想在丹麦）。
工厂窗子的歌儿唱完啦。

---

③ 本行＝I think something is rotten in Denmark. 其实，在诗人的心目中，这些被打破窗子的当然是美国工厂，但他故意说"丹麦"，这就更具有讽刺意味，更耐人寻思。

THE NEW NEGRO[①]

He scans the world with calm and fearless eyes,

    Conscious within of powers long since forgot;[②]

At every step, new man-made barriers rise

    To bar his progress—but he heeds them not.

He stands erect, though tempests round him crash,

    Though thunder bursts and billows surge and roll;

He laughs and forges on, while lightnings flash

    Along the rocky pathway to his goal.

Impassive as a Sphinx, he stares ahead—

    Foresees new empires rise and old ones fall;

While caste-mad nations lust for blood to shed,[③]

    He sees God's finger writing on the wall.[④]

With soul awakened, wise and strong he stands,

Holding his destiny within his hands.

---

① The New Negro：本世纪20年代,美国黑人曾掀起被称为"新黑人运动的哈莱姆文艺复兴"的创作高潮,不少黑人作家和艺术家塑造有觉悟的黑人形象,本诗所描绘的就是这种形象之一。这是一首莎士比亚式十四行诗。

② Conscious within of：Conscious of,意识到；within 是插入的副词,修饰 Conscious。long since forgot：早已被忘却的。forgot 修饰 powers。

新　黑　人

他平静无畏的眼睛审度世界，

　　意识到他被忘却很久的力量，

每步都出现的新的人为障碍

　　阻挡他前进，但不在他的心上。

他傲然挺立，任他的周围霹雳

　　和暴风雨肆虐，大海翻腾怒涛；

道道闪电下，他笑着稳步走去，

　　沿着山岩间的小径走向目标。

像狮身人面像泰然凝看前方，

　　他预见王国的兴起或者衰败；

嗜血的种族为了特权而疯狂，

　　他却见上帝的手在墙上书写。

他站着，种族自豪感已经苏醒，

明智、坚强地掌握着自已命运。

---

③　caste-mad：(白人)为种族特权而疯狂的。

④　God's finger writing on the wall：上帝用手指把神秘的文字写在墙上，宣告暴君的
　　灭亡，见《圣经·旧约·但以理书》第5章。

LET ME LIVE OUT MY YEARS

Let me live out my years in heat of blood!
Let me lie drunken with the dreamer's wine!
Let me not see the soul-house built of mud
Go toppling to the dust—a vacant shrine. [①]

Let me go quickly, like a candle light
Snuffed out just at the heyday of its glow. [②]
Give me high noon—and let it then be night!
Thus would I go.

And grant that when I face the grisly Thing, [③]
My song may trumpet down the grey Perhaps. [④]
O let me be a tune-swept fiddle string
That feels the Master Melody—and snaps!

---

① a vacant shrine 是 Go toppling 的表语, 和 die a hero(死为英雄)的语法结构相同。这
一节曾被美国作家杰克·伦敦用作他的名著《马丁·伊登》的题诗, 这一节译文采自
吴劳先生的这一译作。

让我在热血沸腾中度此一生

让我在热血沸腾中度此一生！
让我在醇酒般的幻梦里醉沉！
莫让我眼见这副泥塑的肉身
倒下时以空虚的躯壳归泥尘。

让我像一支蜡烛突然间熄灭，
让它光华四射时给掐掉烛芯。
让我像正午，让它接着是黑夜！
这样去，我才称心。

面对死神时，让我的歌像号角
能够响彻那灰暗的未知世界。
让我是提琴的琴弦倾泻曲调——
体验那至美旋律时啪地断却！

---

② heyday：全盛期，正旺盛。

③ grant that...：让(我的心愿等)实现吧。

④ perhaps：这里是名词，是"假定，尚属疑问的事物"的意思。

IT COULDN'T BE DONE

Somebody said that it couldn't be done,
　　But he with a chuckle, replied
That "maybe it couldn't", but he would be one
　　Who wouldn't say so till he tried.
So he buckled right in with a trace of a grin①
　　On his face. If he worried he hid it.
He started to sing as he tackled the thing
　　That couldn't be done—and he did it. ②

Somebody scoffed:"Oh, you'll never do that;
　　At least no one ever has done it. "
But he took off his coat and he took off his hat,
　　And the first thing we knew he'd begun it.
With the lift of his chin, and a bit of a grin,
　　Without any doubting or quiddit.
He started to sing as he tackled the thing
　　That couldn't be done, and he did it.

There are thousands to tell you it cannot be done;
　　There are thousands to prophesy failure;
There are thousands to point out to you, one by one,
　　The dangers that wait to assail you.
But just buckle in with a bit of a grin,
　　Just take off your coat and go to it;
Just start to sing as you tackle the thing③
　　That "cannot be done", and you'll do it.

---

① grin:与行内的 in 押韵,下两行中有 thing 和 sing 在行内押韵,称为行内韵,前已屡
　　见。第2、第3节中同此。

这不可能完成

曾有谁说过，这事不可能完成。
　　可是，他只是格格一笑说：
也许这是不可能，不过他这人
　　不愿这么说，除非他试过。
于是他投身其中，微微带笑容；
　　任但心，脸上也不露半分。
他一边干起来，一边唱起歌来；
　　干不成的事情，他已完成。

有人冷言道，"你呀永远干不成；
　　至少，这至今还没人成功。"
可是他把帽一脱，把外套一扔；
　　我们只知道，他已在行动。
他昂首挺胸，脸上露一点笑容，
　　没片刻迟疑，没半句争论。
他一边干起来，一边唱起歌来；
　　干不成的事情，他已完成。

千百人会说，这事不可能完成；
　　千百人会预言你的失败；
千百人会一个一个向你指明，
　　有多少艰险在把你等待。
可只要投身其中，露一点笑容，
　　外套一脱，就干起了事情；
只要一边干起来，一边唱起来；
　　干不成的事情，你将完成。

---

② he did it：他成功了；do it 作"获得成功"解。

③ start：[口] 开始，着手，是习语。

HIS CROSS

He burned no fiery cross
   To frighten men at night；
He bore his burning pain
   In sharpest noonday light；
He wore no hiding mask
   Below his crown of thorn；[①]
He healed the flesh of men
   Whose flesh by men was torn.

He offered love to all
   And took with soul unbowed[②]
Jeering，abuse，and blows，
   The spittle of the crowd.
How strange it is that men
   Should lift his banner high
When they go out to kill[③]
   As he went out to die！

---

①   crown of thorn：荆冠；耶稣被钉上十字架前，被人戴上用荆棘编成的冠冕以嘲弄
    他，并打骂他，用唾沫吐他等等，均见《圣经·新约》诸《福音》书的末后部分。又：西方
    执行死刑时，面部常被遮住，故有 hiding mask。

他的十字架

他从不为了吓唬人
　　晚上烧起火十字架；
他忍受火辣辣痛苦，
　　在午间猛烈阳光下；
他头上戴着个荆冠，
　　没面罩把他脸遮盖；
他治疗人们的创伤——
　　这创伤是人为伤害。

他把爱给了一切人，
　　但是他不屈的灵魂
得忍受打骂和唾沫，
　　得忍受众人的嘲弄。
事情可真是多奇怪：
　　他当初是出发去死，
可现在人们去杀人
　　竟高举着他的旗帜！

---

② 本行＝And took with unbowed soul；took 的宾语是 Jeering，abuse，blows 和 spittle。

③ 这里与本诗第1、2、5行呼应，因为三 K 党在夜间行动时，要点燃十字架，并穿着蒙面罩袍。

THE JUNGLE[①]

It is not the still weight
of the trees, the
breathless interior of the wood,
tangled with wrist-thick

vines, the flies, reptiles,[②]
the forever fearful monkeys
screaming and running
in the branches—

                    but

a girl waiting
shy, brown soft-eyed—
to guide you
              Upstairs, sir.[③]

---

① 丛林,转义为"为生存而残酷斗争的地方",因而 jungle law 意即"弱肉强食的原则"。本诗写的一个年轻女子就是这个"丛林"社会中的一块"弱肉"。而诗中的"说话人"也正在进入"丛林"。

② tangled with wrist-thick/vines：这个过去分词短语修饰 wood,不但跨行,而且跨节;跨节在诗中不足为奇,后面单独一个"but"悬空在第2节和第3节之间却是比较不寻常的,但新诗中原是无所不可,无奇不有的。

丛　林

这并不是树木
沉甸甸的重量、
林中的憋闷、
手腕粗的绕枝乱藤，

不是虻蝇、爬行动物，
也不是树枝间
奔逃尖叫、永远在
担惊受怕的猴群——

　　　　而是

一个等着的腼腆姑娘，
她皮肤棕色，眼光柔和——
在等着领你
　　　　上楼，先生。

---

③ 请注意全篇，除篇首第一个词大写开首外，其余各行皆小写开首，而独 Upstairs。突
　然用大写开首，而且后面有呼语"sir"；所以这一句话可理解为＝to guide you up-
　stairs，saying，"Upstairs，sir."

PROLETARIAN PORTRAIT

A big young bareheaded woman[①]
in an apron

Her hair slicked back standing[②]
on the street

One stockinged foot toeing
the sidewalk[③]

Her shoe in her hand. Looking[④]
intently into it

She pulls out the paper insole
to find the nail

That has been hurting her.

---

① 本诗从开首到第4节的 Her shoe in her hand,是一个以名词 woman 为中心词的单
　部句,也称"名词句"。

② Her hair slicked back,是独立结构,修饰 standing, standing 修饰 woman。

无产者肖像

一个没戴帽的高大少妇
系着围裙

她头发油光光地朝后梳
人站在街边

一只穿长统袜的脚踮在
人行道上

手拿着脱下来的鞋。她仔细
朝那鞋里看

一边抽出垫底的硬纸
想要找到

那只扎痛她的钉子。

---

③　本节又是独立结构；stockinged，是名词 stocking（长袜）＋-ed 构成的形容词；side-walk，人行道，是美国话，在英国称 pavement。

④　Her shoe in her hand：名词＋介词短语，作状语，称为"复合结构"，可以理解为 with her shoe in hand。

NANTUCKET[①]

Flowers through the window
lavender and yellow

changed by white curtains—[②]
Smell of cleanliness—

Sunshine of late afternoon—
On the glass tray

a glass pitcher, the tumbler
turned down, by which

a key is lying—And the
immaculate white bed

---

① Nantucket[næn'tʌkit]，楠塔基特岛，在马萨诸塞州北海岸，避暑胜地。全诗用一连
串名词短语列举室内景物，没有一个谓语动词。

楠塔基特岛

一朵朵花儿透过窗
淡幽幽的紫与鹅黄

因为白窗帘而变幻——
洁净又爽人的清香——

近黄昏时分的阳光——
在那只玻璃托盘上

是只带柄的玻璃罐，
倒放的玻璃杯，一旁

横着把钥匙——还有
那一尘不染的白床

---

② changed：是过去分词。

OVER THE ROOFS

I said, "I have shut my heart,
  As one shuts an open door,
That Love may starve therein[①]
  And trouble me no more."

But over the roofs there came
  The wet new wind of May,
And a tune blew up from the curb
  Where the street-pianos play.

My room was white with the sun
  And Love cried out in me,
"I am strong, I will break your heart[②]
  Unless you set me free."

从大片屋顶上

"像把开着的门关上，"
　　　我说，"我把心也一关，
让爱神在心里饿死，
　　　别再来找我的麻烦。"

但是从大片屋顶上
　　　新吹来湿润五月风，
但是从街沿上飘来
　　　手摇风琴的曲调声。

我屋里阳光一片白，
　　　我心里爱神在喊叫：
"我很强，快放我自由，
　　　要不，把你心撞碎掉。"

---

② break your heart：这里是双关语，既作"打碎你的心"，又作转义的"使你伤心"。

WAR TIME

There will come soft rains and the smell of the ground,
And swallows circling with their shimmering sound;①

And frogs in the pools singing at night,
And wild plum-trees in tremulous white.

Robins will wear their feathery fire②
Whistling their whims on a low-fence-wire;

And not one will know of the war, not one
Will care at last when it is done. ③

Not one would mind, neither bird nor tree,④
If mankind perished utterly;

And Spring herself, when she woke at dawn
Would scarcely know that we were gone. ⑤

---

① swallows：和下节中的 frogs 和 plum-trees 都是篇首 will come 的主语。

② feathery fire＝fiery feathers，倒转的说法不但形象更鲜明，而且 fire 可与下行的
wire 押韵。

③ when it is done＝when the war finishes.

战　时

将会有细雨和大地的气息，
有盘旋的呢喃燕子在闪熠；

水塘里将满是夜啼的青蛙，
野李树将颤动着满枝白花。

知更鸟的毛羽像火焰一样，
将在低围栏上任情地歌唱；

到头来，等这一场战争结束，
对这事没谁会知道、会在乎。

哪怕是全人类已消灭殆尽，
鸟和树都不会为此而操心；

待拂晓时春之神一觉醒来，
她几乎不知道我们已不在。

---

④　neither bird nor tree：与 not one 同位，这里因 bird 和 tree 并列，故可用单数而无需
冠词。
⑤　were gone＝上节的 perished。

DEBT

What do I owe to you

   Who loved me deep and long?[①]

You never gave my spirit wings

   Or gave my heart a song.

But oh, to him I loved,[②]

   Who loved me not at all,

I owe the open gate

   That led through heaven's wall.

---

① deep and long：两个都是副词。

债

你爱我爱得深又久，

　　可是我欠你什么呢？

对我的灵魂我的心，

　　你没给翅膀没给歌。

但对于我所爱的他，

　　我倒是欠下了情份：

他为他并不爱的我，

　　开启了通天堂的门。

---

② to him：承接后面的 I owe。I loved 前面省略 whom。

THE EAGLE AND THE MOLE

Avoid the reeking herd,[①]
Shun the polluted flock,
Live like that stoic bird,
The eagle of the rock.

The huddled warmth of crowds
Begets and foster hate;
He keeps, above the clouds,
His cliff inviolate.[②]

When flocks are folded warm,[③]
And herds to shelter run,[④]
He sails above the storm,
He stares into the sun.

If in the eagle's track[⑤]
Your sinews cannot leap,
Avoid the lathered pack,[⑥]
Turn from the steaming sheep.

---

① herd：多指牛群，下行的 flock 多指羊群。
② inviolate 是上行 keeps his cliff 的宾语补足语，作"不受侵犯"及"不被玷污"解。
③ ate folded：被关进羊栏(fold)里。

山鹰和鼹鼠

避开臭烘烘的牛群，
躲着脏乎乎的群羊；
你活着要像只山鹰，
像那坚忍的鸟一样。

拥挤在一起暖乎乎，
却引起仇恨的滋长；
而鹰窝不会被玷污，
因为它筑在云崖上。

羊进了温暖的羊圈，
牛奔去找藏身地方，
这时在暴风雨上面，
阳光中鹰凝目翱翔。

倘你的筋腱不够强，
难以学山鹰的飞行，
就撇下冒汗气的羊，
就避开淌汗的牛群。

---

④　to shelter run ＝run to shelter.

⑤　in the track of...：步……的后尘，学……的样，是习语。

⑥　lathered ['lɑːðəd]：(马等) 身上布满汗珠(lather)的。

If you would keep your soul
From spotted sight or sound,
Live like the velvet mole;[7]
Go burrow underground. [8]

And there hold intercourse[9]
With roots of trees and stones,
With rivers at their source,
And disembodied bones. [10]

---

⑦   velvet mole：天鹅绒般柔软光滑的鼹鼠。

⑧   Go burrow＝Go to burrow.

不妙的声音和景象，
你若要灵魂不污秽，
就学柔滑鼹鼠的样，
去把洞打在地下面。

那里有树根和石块，
有江河溪涧的源头
和已没有肉的骨骸：
你就去交这些朋友。

---

⑨　hold intercourse with：同……交往。

⑩　disembodied：脱离了肉体的。

PROPHECY

I shall lie hidden in a hut
　　In the middle of an alder wood,
With the back door blind and bolted shut,①
　　And the front door locked for good.②

I shall lie folded like a saint,
　　Lapped in a scented linen sheet,
On a bedstead striped with bright-blue paint,
　　Narrow and cold and neat.

The midnight will be glassy black
　　Behind the panes, with wind about ③
To set his mouth against a crack
　　And blow the candle out.

---

① 　bolted shut：关门落闩。这一行里 back, blind, bolted 三个 b 开首的词都处于重读
　　("扬")的位置，头韵突出，读来似闻关门落闩的砰嘭之声。

预　言

在一片赤杨树林的中间，
　　有间屋把躺着的我藏匿；
它堵死的后门下了门闩，
　　前门也永远锁起。

我将被包得像圣徒一样，
　　薰香的亚麻被单裹一条，
躺在翠蓝条纹的床架上，
　　细狭洁净又冷峭。

窗玻璃外面将昏沉漆黑，
　　午夜时只听得风声呼啸；
它要找一条墙缝凑上嘴，
　　吹得那残烛灭掉。

② for good：一劳永逸，永远，也作 for good and all。
③ wind about：风在周围呼啸。这里的 about 是副词。

CALIBAN IN THE COAL MINES[①]

God, we don't like to complain!
　　We know that the mine is no lark.
But—there's the pools from the rain![②]
　　But—there's the cold and the dark.

God, You don't know what it is—
　　You, in Your well-lighted sky—
Watching the meteors whizz!
　　Warm, with a sun always by.[③]

God, if You had but the moon
　　Stuck in Your cap for a lamp,
Even You'd tire of it soon,
　　Down in the dark and the damp.

Nothing but blackness above[④]
　　And nothing that moves but the cars.
God, if you wish for our love,
　　Fling us a handful of stars!

---

① Caliban：卡力班，原为莎士比亚剧本《暴风雨》中为 prospero 干粗活的半兽人，详见前面 Lanier 诗 *Marsh Song—at Sunset* 注 1，这里借喻美国矿工。

② there's the pools：这里的 there's 是俚语，＝there're (there are)。

煤矿中的卡力班

上帝呀，我们不喜欢抱怨！
　　　我们知道矿里并不好玩。
但这里是雨水积成的潭！
　　　但这里只有寒冷和黑暗。

你哪知道这是什么滋味——
　　　你在那亮堂堂的天堂里
注视着流星在飕飕地飞！
　　　温暖的太阳总是陪着你。

上帝呀，要是你只有月亮
　　　安在你帽子上算是灯盏，
在下面又暗又湿这地方，
　　　即使你也会很快就厌倦。

只有些煤车在来来去去，
　　　头上是骏黑骏黑的坑顶。
上帝呀，如果要我们爱你，
　　　那就给我们撒一把星星！

---

③　Warm：修饰本节第 2 行的 You。

④　Nothing but：除……外什么也没有（或什么也不是），只有，只不过。

AN IMMORALITY

Sing we for love and idleness,[①]
Naught else is worth the having.[②]

Though I have been in many a land,
There is naught else in living.[③]

And I would rather have my sweet,
Though rose-leaves die of grieving,

Than do high deeds in Hungary[④]
To pass all men's believing.[⑤]

---

① Sing we=Let's sing.
② Naught else=Nothing else. worth the having：与 worth having 的不同之处在于用了 the，表示动作已经实现。

劣 行 一 桩

我们为爱和闲散歌唱，
享有这些抵得过一切。

虽说我到过许多地方，
生活中最妙就数这些。

尽管玫瑰瓣死于伤心，
我宁有恋人相伴相偕，

决计不肯远去匈牙利
干出令人难信的大业。

---

③ There is naught else in living：生活中除了 love and idleness 都没有意思。

④ Than：与上节第 1 行 rather 呼应。rather...than...：宁可……而不要……

⑤ 本行意为：(伟大得)使人难以置信。

SALUTATION

O generation of the thoroughly smug

     and thoroughly uncomfortable,

I have seen fishermen picnicking in the sun,

I have seen them with untidy families,[①]

I have seen their smiles full of teeth

     and heard ungainly laughter.

And I am happier than you are,[②]

And they were happier than I am;[③]

And the fish swim in the lake

     and do not even own clothing.

---

① families：家属，也单指子女。
② you：指篇首的诗人向他们招呼的那个 generation。

致　敬

　　啊,完全心满意足的一代

　　　　和心情极为不安的一代,

　　我见过渔民们在阳光下野餐,

　　我见过他们带着邂逅的家人,

　　我见过他们露出满口牙的笑容

　　　　并听到他们粗鲁的大笑声。

　　我呀,比你们幸福,

　　而他们比我幸福;

　　鱼儿在湖中遨游,

　　　　却连衣服也没有。

---

③ they:指 fishermen。

THE GARDEN

Like a skein of loose silk blown against a wall
She walks by the railing of a path in Kensington Gardens. ①
And she is dying piece-meal of a sort of emotional anemia. ②

And round about her there is a rabble
Of the filthy, sturdy, unkillable infants of the very poor. ③
They shall inherit the earth.

In her is the end of breeding.
Her boredom is exquisite and excessive.
She would like someone to speak to her,
And is almost afraid that I will commit that indiscretion. ④

---

① Kensington ['kenziŋtən] Gardens：(在伦敦西部上流社会住宅区的)肯辛顿花园，原
为肯辛顿宫的庭园，18 世纪改为公园。

② is dying piece-meal of：逐渐地死于(某种疾病或某种原因)；piece-meal，一片一片
地，一点一点地，＝by piecemeal。

肯辛顿公园

像一团散乱的丝被吹在墙上，
她走在肯辛顿公园的小径栏杆旁。
而她正渐渐死于一种感情的贫血症。

在她的四周有着一帮子
肮脏、结实、死不了的穷人家小孩。
他们将继承这个世界。

她身上的教养到了终点。
她的厌烦优雅又过度。
她倒想有个人同她说说话，
却几乎又担心我会干出这轻率事来。

---

③　infants：婴儿，也指少年儿童。

④　commit that indiscretion [indis'kreʃən]：干出那种轻率事，指去跟她搭话。

LINCOLN①

Like a gaunt, scraggly pine②
Which lifts its head above the mournful sandhills;
And patiently, through dull years of bitter silence,
Untended and uncared for, starts to grow. ③

Ungainly, laboring, huge,④
The wind of the north has twisted and gnarled its branches;
Yet in the heat of mid-summer days, when thunder clouds
    ring the horizon,⑤
A nation of men shall rest beneath its shade.

And it shall protect them all,
Hold everyone safe there, watching aloof in silence;
Until at last, one mad stray bolt from the zenith
Shall strike it in an instant down to earth.

---

① 本诗原来共四章,这是第一章,也是最短的一章。
② 本行前面省略 Lincoln is。
③ Untended and uncared for:两个过去分词作状语,描述 starts to grow 时的情况。

林　肯

有如一棵枝叶蓬乱的枯瘦松树
在悲凉的沙丘上抬起头来，
默默地熬过沉闷而辛酸的岁月，
虽得不到照料和关心，已开始成长。

模样粗拙、苦苦挣揣、形体巨大；
北风使它的枝干扭扭曲曲，长满了疙瘩；
可在仲夏的暑气里，当挟着风雷的云围拢在天际，
全国的人可以歇在它的树荫之下。

它会护住他们，使每个人在它荫下安然无恙，
而高高的它却默默地注视着远方；
直到最后，当空一个狂乱的霹雳，
竟霎时间把它劈倒在地。

---

④　本行可理解为前面省略 The pine is。

⑤　thunder clouds ring the horizon：雷云围拢在地平线上；这里 ring 略似李贺诗句"黑云压城城欲摧"中的"压"字。

LETHE[①]

Nor skin nor hide nor fleece[②]
   Shall cover you,
Nor curtain of crimson nor fine
Shelter of cedar-wood be over you,[③]
    Nor the fir-tree
    Nor the pine.[④]

Nor sight of whin nor gorse[⑤]
    Nor river-yew,
Nor fragrance of flowering bush,
Nor wailing of reed-bird to waken you.
    Nor of linnet
    Nor of thrush.[⑥]

Nor word nor touch nor sight
    Of lover, you
Shall long through the night but for this:[⑦]
The roll of the full tide to cover you
    Without question,
    Without kiss.

---

① Lethe['li:θi(:)]:[希腊神话]冥河,也译"忘川",谓亡灵饮其水,即忘却其尘世间的
   一切往事。

② Nor...nor...;[古、诗]=Neither...nor....

③ be:承前,=shall be.

冥　河

没有皮肤、兽皮或毛皮
　　会把你盖住，
没绯红帷幕或雪松树丛
会作为精妙的屏障把你遮住，
　　也没有枞树，
　　没有青松。

眼前没芒柄花、荆豆，
　　没河边杉影，
没灌木树丛的花朵香味，
没芦苇鸟的哀叫声把你唤醒。
　　也没有红雀，
　　没有画眉。

没一句话、一次触摸，
　　没情人目光，
长夜中你将只把这渴求：
让滚滚的满潮涌来把你盖上，
　　问题没一个，
　　吻也没有。

---

④　这两行和前面一连串的 nor...nor 并列。

⑤　Nor sight：前面省略 There shall be，补上这个谓语，则全节成为一个完全句。

⑥　这两行承上行，＝Nor wailing of linnet, nor wailing of thrush to waken you.

⑦　本行中 long for，渴望，企求；but ＝only；this 指后面所说的内容。

COMMON DUST

And who shall separate the dust
   Which later we shall be：
Whose keen discerning eye will scan
   And solve the mystery?

The high，the low，the rich，the poor，
   The black，the white，the red，
And all the chromatique between，①
   Or whom shall it be said：

"Here lies the dust of Africa；
   Here are the sons of Rome；②
Here lies one unlabeled，
   the world at large his home"?

Can one then separate the dust，
   Will mankind lie apart，③
When life has settled back again
   The same as from the start?④

---

① chromatique：法语词，相当于 chromatic，这里加 the 后，指肤色介于黑、白、红之间的
   人，如各种程度的混血儿等。

② sons of Rome：罗马的子孙。这里特地用罗马，令人从煊赫一时的古罗马帝国的兴
   亡，联想到千古英雄人物。

同　是　尘　土

到时候我们将化作尘土，
　　谁还能把我们区别？
谁的眼睛分辨力特别强，
　　一看便把这谜剖解？

高贵者卑贱者，富翁穷汉，
　　黑人白人印第安人
和介于其间的各色人种——
　　哪里还能够说得准：

"这是非洲人化成的尘土，
　　这些人祖藉是罗马；
这里的一个没什么标签，
　　全世界便是他的家"？

当生命之躯重归于尘土，
　　同起初的时候一样，
那时谁还能把尘土区分？
　　人还会各躺在一方？

---

③　mankind：人类，前面不用 the，常被用作复数，有时也作单数用。

④　基督教认为人原本是泥土，死了复归泥土。

TRIUMPH OF LOVE

I shake my hair in the wind of morning
  For the joy within me that knows no bounds,[1]
I echo backward the vibrant beauty[2]
  Wherewith heaven's hollow lute resounds.[3]

I shed my song on the feet of all men,
  On the feet of all shed out like wine,
On the whole and the hurt I shed my bounty,
  The beauty within me that is not mine.

Turn not away from my song, nor scorn me,
  Who bear the secret that holds the sky
And the stars together, but know within me[4]
  There speaks another more wise than I.[5]

Nor spurn me here from your heart, to hate me![6]
  Yet hate me here if you will—not so
Myself you hate, but the Love within me[7]
  That loves you, whether you would or no.[8]

Here love returns with love to the lover,
  And beauty unto the heart thereof,[9]
And hatred unto the heart of the hater,
  Whether he would or no, with love!

---

① knows no bounds：无限。

② echo backward：对……发出回响。

③ Wherewith = With which，它所引起的是一个限制性定语从句，修饰 the vibrant beauty；这两行的意思是：我对美妙的天籁发出回响（即唱歌）。

④ know within me：know 后省略 that；within me 是 that 引起的从句里的修饰词。

⑤ more wise：一般说，比 wiser 语气较强，在诗中则有格律关系，wiser 为"扬抑"，more wise "扬抑"或"抑扬"均可。

爱神的凯旋

我让早晨的风儿吹动我头发，
　　因为我心中的欢乐海阔天广；
苍穹这诗琴发出美妙的声波，
　　对于这天籁我也发出了回响。

我把歌朝所有的人脚上洒去，
　　洒在所有的人脚上算是美酒——
我向完好者、伤者散发这厚礼，
　　因为我心中的美不归我占有。

别嫌弃我的歌，也别看不起我，
　　我可怀着把天空和星星联系
在一起的秘密；要知道还有位
　　比我聪明者的话响在我心里。

别因为恨我就赶我出你的心！
　　如果你决意恨我，就请这样做：
是爱神不问你态度，始终爱你——
　　你是恨我心中的爱神，不恨我。

这样，爱就添上爱回到了爱者，
　　同时还有美回到爱者的心灵；
而不管恨者愿意还是不愿意，
　　回到他心头的是添上爱的恨。

---

⑥　spurn me here：这里的 here 用在名词或代词后加强语气，无甚实义。to hate me：以
　　表示恨我。

⑦　not so...，but...：与其说……，不如说……。

⑧　whether you would or no＝Whether you would or not；whether or no 可作"无论如
　　何"解。

⑨　thereof ＝of that，这里＝of the lover。

A TALISMAN[①]

Under a splintered mast,
torn from the ship and cast
　　　　near her hull,

a stumbling shepherd found,
embedded in the ground,[②]
　　　　a sea-gull

of lapis lazuli,
a scarab of the sea,[③]
　　　　with wings spread—[④]

curling its coral feet,
parting its beak to greet
　　　　men long dead.[⑤]

---

① 本诗分四节,节节相连,构成一个句子,其中心部分为:a shepherd found a sea-gull
　of lapis lazuli ['læpis'læzjulai],余皆修饰语。
② 是插在 found 和 a sea-gull 之间的分词短语,修饰 sea-gull of lapis lazuli。

一 个 护 符

离船身不远的地方，
那支桅折断在地上，
　　已残碎支离；

牧羊人在那里一绊，
发现断桅下的地面
　　埋着件东西：

那是天青石的海鸥，
是海上甲虫形石符；
　　它张着翅膀，

蜷缩着珊瑚般双脚，
张着嘴向人们问好——
　　人早已死亡。

---

③　scarab['skærəb]：（古代埃及人刻在石块上作护符的）圣甲虫，是 sea-gull of lapis
　　lazuli 的同位语。

④　spread：过去分词，修饰 wings。

⑤　men long dead：long dead 是后置定语，修饰 men。

THE MIND IS AN ENCHANTING THING[1]

    is an enchanted thing
        like the glaze on a
    katydid-wing[2]
           subdivided by sun
           till the nettings are legion. [3]
    Like Gieseking playing Scarlatti;[4]

    like the apteryx-awl
        as a beak, or the
    kiwi's rain-shawl
           of haired feathers, the mind
           feeling its way as though blind,[5]
    Walks along with its eyes on the ground.

    It has memory's ear
        that can hear without
    having to hear.
           Like the gyroscope's fall,[6]
           truly, unequivocal[7]
    because trued by regnant certainty,[8]

---

① 这是本诗的标题,同时又作为诗的第 1 行。本诗另一特点是:诗句以音节而不是音
   步建行,各节相应行的音节数一致;且各节的 1、3 行和 4、5 行分别押韵。

② katydid['keitidid]:美洲大螽斯。

③ are legion:极多,无数,是习语。

④ Gieseking ['giːzəkiŋ]:德国钢琴家,Scarlatti:意大利作曲家。

智力是一种迷人的东西

是一种着迷的东西
　　像大螽斯翅膀上
那层光亮的翳
　　　　被阳光分隔再分隔
　　　　直分到网络无穷地多。
像基塞金奏斯卡拉蒂的作品；

像无翼鸟形的尖锥
　　　　有如是鸟喙，或像
毛茸茸的几维
　　　　有着可挡雨的披巾，
　　　　智力像盲者摸索前进，
行动时总是把眼睛朝着地上。

它有着回忆的耳朵
　　　　这耳朵能听，然而
不是非听不可。
　　　　像是倾斜的陀螺仪，
　　　　真是那样的明确无疑，
因为凭强有力的确定性校准，

---

⑤　as though blind＝as though it（the mind）were blind.

⑥　gyroscope's［'gairəskəups 或'dʒairəskəups］fall：陀螺仪的着力点。

⑦　truly：确实，这里是插入语。

⑧　trued：(安装，调整等)摆正，校准。

it is a power of
      strong enchantmant. It
is like the dove-
      neck animated by
      sun; it is memory's eye;
It's conscientious inconsistency.

It tears off the veil; tears
      the temptation, the
mist the heart wears,
      from its eyes,—if the heart
      has a face; it takes apart
dejection. It's fire in the dove-neck's

iridescence, in the
      inconsistencies
of Scarlatti.
      Unconfusion submits
      its confusion to proof; it's
not a Herod's oath that cannot change.[9]

---

⑨　Herod's ['herədz] oath：希律王的誓言；犹太王 Herod Antipas（? 一公元 39 年后）
生日，她女儿翩翩翩起舞，为他祝寿，王大悦，发誓说她要什么就赏赐什么，她说要施
洗者约翰的头，王即下令取下关押在宫中的约翰的首级，盛在盘上端来赐给她（见
《圣经·新约·马太福音》第 14 章第 3—11 节）。

这是有强大魅力的
　　　一种力量。这就像
阳光照耀下的
　　　　　呈异彩的鸽子脖颈；
　　　它是回忆具有的眼睛；
它是煞费苦心的不协调之处。

它撕掉面纱；它撕破
　　　罩着心灵的迷蒙——
它眼前的诱惑——
　　　　　就是说，倘心灵有脸
　　　　　的话，它把沮丧全拆散。
它是火，在鸽子脖颈的虹彩中，

在斯卡拉蒂作品里
　　　那些不协调之中。
不混乱把它的
　　　　　混乱交出去受检验；
　　　　　这不是希律王的誓言，
所以不是没有改变余地的。

BLUE GIRLS

Twirling your blue skirts, travelling the sward
Under the towers of your seminary,
Go listen to your teachers old and contrary
Without believing a word.

Tie the white fillets then about your hair
And think no more of what will come to pass[1]
Than bluebirds that go walking on the grass[2]
And chattering on the air.

Practise your beauty, blue girls, before it fail;
And I will cry with my loud lips and publish
Beauty which all our power shall never establish,
It is so frail.

For I could tell you a story which is true;
I know a lady with a terrible tongue,
Blear eyes fallen from blue,
All her perfections tarnished—yet it is not long
Since she was lovelier than any of you.

---

① come to pass：发生，实现，是习语。

蓝衣姑娘们

在你们女校的这些高房子之下，
旋转起你们的蓝裙子，穿过草地——
任教师是老是少，听不进一个字，
但你们还是去听课吧。

随即用一条白头带把头发一扎，
将来会发生什么事就不要去想，
只想幸福的青鸟在草地上来往
又在半空中叽叽喳喳。

在美衰退前，快运用你们的美吧；
蓝衣姑娘们，我要用我响亮的嘴
来宣扬我们无力使之常驻的美，
它真是太脆弱啦。

因为我能够告诉你们真事一件：
我认识一位嘴令人敬畏的女士，
昏花的眼丧失了蔚蓝，
她全部的美已失去光彩，但是，
不久前她比你们哪一位都鲜艳。

---

② bluebirds：青色的鸟，特指美国产的学名为 *Sialia Sialis* 的青鸟，幸福的象征。

BELLS FOR JOHN WHITESIDE'S DAUGHTER

There was such speed in her little body,
And such lightness in her footfall,
It is no wonder her brown study①
Astonishes us all.

Her wars were bruited in our high window.
We looked among orchard trees and beyond,②
Where she took arms against her shadow,③
Or harried unto the pond④

The lazy geese, like a snow cloud
Dripping their snow on the green grass,
Tricking and stopping, sleepy and proud,
Who cried in goose, Alas,⑤

For the tireless heart within the little
Lady with rod that made them rise
From their noon apple-dreams and scuttle⑥
Goose-fashion under the skies!

But now go the bells, and we are ready,
In one house we are sternly stopped
To say we are vexed at her brown study,
Lying so primly propped. ⑦

---

① brown study: 沉思,呆呆出神;常用于 in a brown study 这一习语中,按 brown 的古
   义为"阴郁的,忧郁的",study 的古义为"沉思,遐想"。

② beyond=beyond orchard trees.

③ took arms against=take up arms (against),拿起武器(对抗)。

④ harried: 赶走,宾语是跨节的 geese。

为约翰·怀赛的女儿敲响的钟

　　她的小小身躯曾那样地敏捷，
　　落地的脚步曾那样轻灵，
　　所以也就难怪她现在的沉思
　　使我们大家都吃惊。

　　在高高窗口我们曾赞她勇敢，
　　曾看着那果树丛的里外，
　　看见她在同自己的影子作战，
　　或是把懒鹅赶起来

　　又逼它们进池塘，像一片雪云
　　把雪洒落在碧绿草地上；
　　它们得意又懒洋洋，走走停停，
　　喝倒彩似地在叫嚷，

　　因为这小姐的心儿不知疲乏，
　　打破它们午间的苹果梦，
　　用棍子赶得它们以鹅的步伐
　　在天空下一路飞奔！

　　可钟现在已响，我们也准备好，
　　在一幢屋里被冷冷挡住，
　　说我们为她那沉思感到苦恼——
　　她躺着，装裹得齐楚。

---

⑤　goose：嘘声，倒彩声，如 get the goose，遭观(听)众喝倒彩。

⑥　apple-dreams：这是诗人自由构词的一例；几乎无所不可的自由构词是英美新诗的
　　特点之一。

⑦　本行中的分词 Lying，不能修饰所有格的 her，按正常英语，前面应补上一个 she，
　　使之成为一个独立结构，描绘她的状态。

AMERICA

Although she feeds me bread of bitterness,
And sinks into my throat her tiger's tooth,
Stealing my breath of life, I will confess
I love this cultured hell that tests my youth!
Her vigor flows like tides into my blood,
Giving me strength erect against her hate. ①
Her bigness sweeps my being like a flood. ②
Yet as a rebel fronts a king in state, ③
I stand within her walls with not a shred
Of terror, malice, not a word of jeer.
Darkly I gaze into the days ahead,
And see her might and granite wonders there, ④
Beneath the touch of Time's unerring hand,
Like priceless treasures sinking in the sand. ⑤

① erect：这里是形容词，作"坚强不屈"解。
② my being：我的存在，我这生存着的人。
③ in state：威严，堂皇。

美　国

尽管她给我吃的是苦涩的面包，
还把她那副虎牙咬进我喉管里
夺了我生命气息，我还是得宣告：
我爱这考验我朝气的文明地狱！
她的活力潮水般涌进了我血液，
给我以力量去反抗她对我的恨。
她的庞大似洪水把我身心冲激。
可我像叛逆同堂堂的国王对阵，
站在他的围墙里却没有丝毫的
恐惧和怨恨，没有一个字的谤讥。
我阴郁地凝望在我前面的日子，
只见她威势和她磐石般的奇迹
在时光永无差错之手的轻触下，
像种种的无价珍宝沉入了泥沙。

---

④　there：这是一首十四行诗，格律谨严，仅这里的 there〔ðεə〕和第10行的 jeer〔dʒiə〕
　　押的是不完全韵。

⑤　sinking in the sand：是前面 see her might and granite wonders 的宾语补足语，看见
　　的不是威势和奇迹，而是它们的沉沦。

AFTERNOON ON A HILL

I will be the gladdest thing①

    Under the sun!

I will touch a hundred flowers

    And not pick one.

I will look at cliffs and clouds②

    With quiet eyes,

Watch the wind bow down the grass,③

    And the grass rise.

And when the lights begin to show

    Up from the town,

I will mark which must be mine,④

    And then start down!

---

① thing：用以指"人"，有爱怜或鄙夷之意。

② cliffs 与 clouds 两词用了头韵，这在诗歌中常见，犹如汉语中的双声，译文中以"云"
和"崖"应之。

小山上的下午

我要自己是天底下

　　最欢的一个！

我要抚摸一百朵花，

　　却不采一朵。

我要以平静的目光

　　看云和崖壁，

看草儿在风中卧倒

　　接着又挺起。

到了下面的市镇中

　　灯光都亮起，

待辩认出我家的灯，

　　我就下山去！

---

③　bow down：使弯倒。

④　mine：我的住处的灯火。

THE DREAM

Love, if I weep it will not matter,
   And if you laugh I shall not care;
Foolish am I to think about it,
   But it is good to feel you there.

Love, in my sleep I dreamed of waking, —
   White and awful the moonlight reached[①]
Over the floor, and somewhere, somewhere
   There was a shutter loose, —it screeched!

Swung in the wind! —and no wind blowing! —[②]
   I was afraid, and turned to you
Put out my hand to you for comfort, —
   And you were gone! Cold, cold as dew,[③]

Under my hand the moonlight lay!
   Love, if you laugh I shall not care,
But if I weep it will not matter, —
   Ah, it is good to feel you there!

---

① reached：伸展。

② Swung：Swing 的过去时，与上节末的 screeched 并列。

梦

亲爱的,倘我哭那并不要紧,
　　我也不在乎你可会大笑;
我也真是傻,竟然会这么想,
　　但感到你在边上可真好。

亲爱的,我睡着时梦见醒来——
　　地板上,惨白惨白的月光
渐渐挨过来,而不知是哪儿
　　松掉的百叶窗在吱嘎响!——

在风中晃荡!却没风在吹!——
　　我感到害怕,朝你转过脸,
向你伸出手,想得到些慰藉——
　　你却不在!而我手的下面

那一滩月光像冷冷的露水!
　　我并不在乎你可会大笑,
亲爱的,倘我哭那也不要紧——
　　感到你在边上啊可真好!

---

③　Cold,cold as dew:跨节作 the moonlight lay 的表语。

ARS POETICA①

A poem should be palpable and mute
As a globed fruit

Dumb
As old medallions to the thumb

Silent as the sleeve-worn stone
Of casement ledges where the moss has grown—

A poem should be wordless
As the flight of birds

                *

A poem should be motionless in time
As the moon climbs

Leaving, as the moon releases
Twig by twig the night-entangled trees,

Leaving, as the moon behind the winter leaves,
Memory by memory the mind—②

A poem should be motionless in time
As the moon climbs

① Ars Poetica [′ɑːz pəu′etikə]＝The Art of Poetry, 诗的艺术, 诗学 (poetics)。本诗
中诗行虽长短不拘, 但基本上两行一韵。

诗　艺

一首诗应当既有实感又沉默
像只圆滚滚水果

它没有声息
像古老的奖章给拇指的感觉

静得像已长出了青苔
早被衣袖磨光的石窗台——

一首诗应当一字不着
像鸟群飞过

*

一首诗应当静止在时间中
像月亮爬上天空

离开时像月亮一个一个枝杈
把树木从夜色的缠绕中解下

离开时像月亮在冬叶的后面
离开心头的一个一个回忆——

一首诗应当静止在时间中
像月亮爬上天空

---

② 本行承上节＝Memory by memory releases the mind；memory by memory 和上节的
twig by twig 都是和习语 one by one 同样的结构，它在这里作状语，修饰 releases。

*

A poem should be equal to:
Not true[③]

For all the history of grief
An empty doorway and a maple leaf

For love
The leaning grasses and two lights above the sea—

A poem should not mean
But be.[④]

---

③　这里的 Not true 可视为是放在括弧内或破折号之间的插入语；equal to 接下节的
　　An empty doorway and a maple leaf 和再下一节的 The leaning grasses and the two
　　lights above the sea，意谓等于(相当于)这些东西，而并不真是列举的这些具体事
　　物的如实写照。

*

一首诗应当相等于:
不是真实

对于所有的悲哀历史
相等于空空的门口和一片枫叶

对于爱情
相等于依偎的草和海上的两盏灯——

一首诗应当不含深意
是诗而已。

④ 这两行意为:诗不应该有什么含意,诗就是诗;这里的 be 是"写出来就是"的意思。

OLD AGE[①]

In me is a little painted square

Bordered by old shops with gaudy awnings.

And before the shops sit smoking, open-bloused old men,[②]

Drinking sunlight.

The old men are my thoughts;

And I come to them each evening, in a creaking cart,

And quietly unload supplies.

We fill slim pipes and chat

And inhale scents from pale flowers in the center of the aquare....

Strong men, tinkling women, and dripping, squealing children

Stroll past us, or into the shops.

They greet the shopkeepers and touch their hats or foreheads to

    me....

Some evening I shall not return to my people.[③]

---

① 本诗标题可与第一行连读。

② sit smoking, open-bloused old men = open-bloused old men sit smoking; open-
bloused, 敞开着短上衣的。

老　年

在我心中是个色彩鲜明的小广场，
四周是张着花俏遮篷的老店铺。
店铺前坐着一个个抽烟老汉——
都敞开着衣襟在吸饮阳光。
这些老汉就是我的思绪；
每天晚上我坐一辆吱嘎作响的大车
来到他们那里，轻轻卸下供应品。
我们把烟丝装满细长的烟斗，闲谈着，
吸着广场中央淡色花朵的香味。……
发丁当声的妇女、汗淋淋的尖叫儿童
和壮汉逛过我们面前，或逛进店铺。
他们向店主问好，向我举手及帽或及额致意。……
总会有一晚，我将不再去见这些朋友。

---

③　本行意谓："总有一天我将死去。"

A LADY COMES TO AN INN

Three strange men came to the inn,
One was a black man pocked and thin,
One was brown with a silver knife,
And one brought with him a beautiful wife.

That lovely woman had hair as pale
As French champagne or finest ale,
That lovely woman was long and slim
As a young white birch or a maple limb.

Her face was like cream, her mouth was a rose,
What language she spoke nobody knows,
But sometimes she'd scream like a cockatoo
And swear wonderful oaths that nobody knew.

Her great silk skirts like a silver bell
Down to her little bronze slippers fell,[1]
And her low-cut gown showed a dove on its nest
In blue tatooing across her breast.

Nobody learned the lady's name
Nor the marvelous land from which they came,
But no one in all the countryside
Has forgotten those men and that beautiful bride.

---

① 本行＝fell down to her little bronze slippers；fell 的主语是 skirts。

一位夫人来到客栈

三个陌生汉子来到客栈；
一个瘦瘦的黑人有麻点，
一个棕皮肤的人带银刀，
另一个有美丽的妻子在一道 。

这美女的头发浅黄淡金，
像上好啤酒或法国香槟；
这美女的身材修长细挑，
像不高的白桦或枫树的枝条。

她面似乳脂，嘴像玫瑰花，
没人知道她讲哪儿的话；
可有时她白鹦鹉般尖叫，
那希奇的咒骂谁都莫名其妙。

丝绸的大裙子宛如银钟，
裙下的软鞋颜色近青铜；
低领口露出她刺花胸膛——
一只蓝色的鸽子栖息在窝上。

没人知道这夫人的名字、
他们属哪一片神奇土地；
但整个这一带没人遗忘
那三个汉子和那美丽的新娘。

ME UP AT DOES[2]

Me up at does

out of the floor

quietly Stare

a poisoned mouse

still who alive

is asking What

have i done that

You wouldn't have

---

[1] 这位诗人写诗常别出心裁，连其本人姓名也小写。所以他大写或小写的词值得注意。

抬头盯视我

抬头盯视我

还没有断气
从地板缝隙

中毒的老鼠

它眼光平静

看来在问我
我干了什么

惹你不高兴

---

② 全诗八行，头五行词序零乱，表示说话人语无伦次。词序虽然零乱，但每行多为四个
音节，且押着近似 abbacddc 的"不完全韵"。其正常的词序可为：A poisoned mouse
who is still alive，does stare（＝stares）up at me quietly out of the floor, asking,
"What have I done that you wouldn't have (done)?"

FACE

Hair—

silver-gray,

like streams of stars,

Brows—

recurved canoes[①]

quivered by the ripples blown by pain,[②]

Her eyes—

mist of tears

condensing on the flesh below

And her channeled muscles

are cluster grapes of sorrow[③]

purple in the evening sun

nearly ripe for worms.

---

①   recurved＝bent backward.

②   quivered：过去分词，修饰 canoes。

脸

头发——

银灰色，

像繁星点点的溪流，

双眉——

两头朝里翘的划子

在痛苦激起的细浪上颤动，

她的眼睛——

泪水的翳

凝聚在那下面的血肉上，

而她布满沟纹的肌肉

是串悲哀的葡萄

紫紫地映着晚照：

已熟得快喂蛆虫。

---

③　cluster grapes：成串的葡萄。

1935

All night they marched, the infantrymen under pack,
But the hands gripping the rifles were naked bone
And the hollow pits of the eyes stared, vacant and black,
When the moonlight shone.

The gas mask lay like a blot on the empty chest,
The slanting helmets were spattered with rust and mold,
But they burrowed the hill for the machine-gun nest
As they had of old. [①]

And the guns rolled, and the tanks, but there was no sound,
Never the gasp or rustle of living men
Where the skeletons strung their wire on disputed ground...
I knew them, then.

"It is seventeen years," I cried. "you must come no more. [②]
We know your names. We know that you are the dead.
Must you march forever from France and the last, blind war?"
"*Fool! From the next* !" they said. [③]

---

① 本行＝As they had burrowed of old; of old, 从前, 是习语。
② It is seventeen years: 从第一次世界大战结束的 1918 年到本诗所吟的 1935 年, 相隔十七年。

一九三五

驮着背包的步兵一整夜都在行进，
可他们握枪的手却是裸露的骨头，
而在茫然凝望的是黑洞洞眼窟窿——
　　　　那是月光照耀的时候。

防毒面具在空荡荡的胸前像污渍，
歪斜戴着的钢盔布满锈迹和霉斑；
他们挖掘着山头，为机枪构筑掩体，
　　　　一如他们从前那样干。

炮声隆隆，坦克在冲，但没一点声响，
也没有活人喘息或衣物窸窣之声——
骷髅们在有争议的地方架铁丝网……
　　　　于是我就认出了他们。

我喊，"有十七年啦；你们千万别再来。
我们知道你们的名字；你们早死掉。
你们老得从法国、从上次混战开来？"
　　　　"傻瓜！从下次战争！"他们道。

---

③　*From the next!*：意谓下次战争还要死人。这是个省略句，其它部分承上行省略了。

THE FARM DIED

I watched the agony of a mountain farm,
a gangrenous decay:
the farm died with the pines that sheltered it;
the farm died when the woodshed rotted away.

It died to the beat of a loose board on the barn[1]
that flapped in the wind all night;
nobody came to drive a nail in it.
The farm died in a broken window-light,[2]

a broken pane upstairs in the guest bedroom,
through which the autumn rain
beat down all night upon the Turkey carpet;
nobody thought to putty in a pane.

Nobody nailed another slat on the corncrib;
nobody mowed the hay;
nobody came to mend the rusty fences.
The farm died when the two boys went away,

or maybe lived till the old man was buried,[3]
but after it was dead I loved it more,
though poison sumac grew in the empty pastures,[4]
though ridgepoles fell, and though November winds
came all night whistling through an open door.

---

[1] to the beat of: 合着……的拍子。

[2] window-light ＝windowpane.

死去的农舍

我细看着山间农舍死去后的惨像，
那是坏疽般的衰败：
这农舍同护着它的松林一起死去；
农舍死去时柴火棚也在朽烂塌坏。

谷仓上松脱的板整夜在风中砰嘭——
农舍按这节拍死亡；
但没有一个人来用钉子把板钉牢。
农舍的死反映在一方碎玻璃窗上——

楼上的客人卧室里一块玻璃碎了，
秋雨就从那窗洞里
整夜地打进来，打在土耳其地毯上；
可没有人想到用油灰粘上块玻璃。

没有人再把板条钉上放玉米的囤；
没有人再收割牧草；
也没有人来修理破破烂烂的栅栏。
这农舍死于两个小伙子离家走掉，

也可说是活到那老汉入土的时候，
但死后的农舍我更爱，
尽管空荡荡的牧场上长起毒漆树，
尽管大梁已塌下，尽管十一月的风
整夜从敞开的门口打着唿哨吹来。

---

③ lived：主语是上节末行的 The farm。

④ poison sumac ['sjuːmæk 或 'ʃuːmæk]：[植]美国毒漆树；sumac 为漆树属植物。

HOME-COMING

When I stepped homeward to my hill
  Dusk went before with quiet tread;
The bare laced branches of the trees
  Were as a mist about its head.

Upon its leaf-brown breast, the rocks
  Like great gray sheep lay silent-wise;[1]
Between the birch trees' gleaming arms
  The faint stars trembled in the skies.

The white brook met me half-way up
  And laughed as one that knew me well,
To whose more clear than crystal voice[2]
  The frost had joined a crystal spell.

The skies lay like pale-watered deep.
  Dusk ran before me to its strand
And cloudily leaned forth to touch
  The moon's slow wonder with her hand.[3]

---

[1] silent-wise=silently; 这里用 wise 显然是为与本节末行的 skies 押韵的需要。

[2] 本行=To whose voice which is more clear than crystal.

回　家

回家时当我走近我那小山，
　　　暮色已悄悄地走到我前面；
穿来插去的光秃秃树枝儿
　　　像薄雾淡霭轻拢在山头边。

山岩如一群静卧的大灰羊，
　　　黄叶般颜色的胸膛贴着地；
白桦树隐隐闪亮的胳臂间
　　　是幽幽的星星在天上颤栗。

我上坡途中，白花花的小溪
　　　像老朋友大笑着把我欢迎；
在它比水晶还清澈的嗓音里
　　　添了水晶般魅力的是薄冰。

天空像水色浅淡的一片海；
　　　暮色在我前面奔向那海滨，
它挟云带烟地探身伸出手，
　　　要把渐露奇妙的月亮触碰。

---

③　The moon's slow wonder：月亮缓缓移动的奇妙景色。

THE HOUND

Life the hound

Equivocal

Comes at a bound

Either to rend me

Or to befriend me.

I cannot tell

The hound's intent

Till he has sprung

At my bare hand

With teeth or tongue. [①]

Meanwhile I stand[②]

And wait the event.

---

① With teeth or tongue: 用牙齿(咬)还是用舌头(舔)。

猎　狗

生活这猎狗

态度暧昧地

朝着我一扑：

不是想咬我

就是要亲热。

这狗的心思

我说不明白，

只看它跳来

对我的光手

是咬还是舔。

我站在那儿

等事态发展。

---

② Meanwhile：在狗还没有向我的手纵身跳起的这一段时间里。

A NARRATIVE

Bill dug a well
And knelt down to it:
Frank bought a telescope
And stared up through it:
Both looking for truth
Since nobody knew it.
Bill sought dark,
No light reflected;[①]
Frank sought light,
With dark neglected.
One looked up,
One looked down;
And a long-drawn fight
Began in our town.
Was Bill in the right
Looking down his well?
Was Frank our hope,
With his telescope?
We could not tell.
But when Frank said
"I find that dark
Is what makes light,"
Bill raised his head;

---

① 这里的 reflected 和下面第二行中的 neglected 都是过去分词,在 No light reflected 前面也可加上个 With。

记 事 一 则

比尔掘了一口井，
双膝着地跪井旁；
弗兰克买了望远镜，
用它朝着天上望；
两人都在找真理——
没谁知道在何方。
比尔找的是黑暗，
没有一点儿反光；
弗兰克找的是光明，
完全忽略了黑暗。
一个朝上望，
一个向下看；
于是我们这地方，
争论就此没个完。
比尔做得可正确，
就为总向井里看？
弗兰克使用望远镜，
是不是我们的希望？
我们说不上。
但当弗兰克说道：
"我发现黑暗
就是发光的地方，"
比尔就会抬起头：

"I can't find night
Without a spark,"
Was what Bill said.
"Let's look at your well,"
Said Frank to Bill;
And Bill looked up
Through the telescope.
"What do you see?"
Said Bill to Frank.
"Stars and an echo of dark,"said Frank. [2]
"What do you see?"
Said Frank to Bill.
"Dark and the echo of stars,"said Bill. [3]
One looked up,
One looked down;
And the fight goes on
All over our town.
Was Bill our hope
At the telescope?
Did Frank do right
To take Bill's well?
No one can tell.
They're at it still.

---

[2]   **Stars and an echo of dark**：Frank 一心找光明，所以在井底看到的也是光明的星星，
而黑暗只是虚影。

吐出一句话：
"黑夜里我可找不到
没一点闪光的地方。"
"让咱看看你的井，"
弗兰克对比尔说道；
比尔就用望远镜
朝着天空里张望。
"你看见什么？"比尔问。
弗兰克答道："星星
和一种黑夜的虚影。"
他也问："你看见什么？"
比尔回答道："黑暗
和一些星星的虚影。"
一个朝上望，
一个向下看；
于是我们这地方
至今争论没个完。
比尔用望远镜看天，
就成了我们的希望？
弗兰克做得可正确，
就为他向那井里看？
没人说得上。
他们还在这样干。

---

③ Dark and the echo of stars；Bill 一心找黑暗，所以他用望远镜观天，所见只是黑暗的
夜空，而把星星只当虚影。与注 2 对照，这两人各自抱着片面的先入之见，岂不是一
副发人深思的绝妙讽刺画？

HARLEM①

What happens to a dream deferred?

Does it dry up
like a raisin in the sun?

Or fester like a sore—②
And then run?

Does it stink like rotten meat?
Or crust and sugar over—③
like a syrupy sweet?④

Maybe it just sags
like a heavy load.

Or does it explode?

---

① Harlem：哈莱姆，纽约黑人区。本诗形式虽较自由，但仍用韵。
② fester：承前，＝does it fester.

哈 莱 姆

梦被推迟实现又会怎么样？

它可会像一粒葡萄干
被阳光晒得干透？

或者像疮开始溃烂——
随后脓血直流？

它可会像烂肉发臭？
或者面上结一层糖壳——
有如糖浆般的甜酒？

也许它像是个重荷
只会渐渐搭拉。

或者它可会爆炸？

---

③　sugar：动词，结成糖块。

④　syrupy[ˈsirəpi] sweet：糖浆状的甜食或甜酒。

HOMESICK BLUES①

De railroad bridge's②
A sad song in de air.
De railroad bridge's
A sad song in de air.
Ever' time de trains pass③
I wants to go somewhere.

I went down to de station;
Ma heart was in ma mouth.④
Went down to de station;
Heart was in ma mouth.
Lookin' for a box car⑤
To roll me to de South.

Homesick blues, Lawd,⑥
'S a terrible thing to have.⑦
Homesick blues is
A terrible thing to have.
To keep from cryin'
I opens ma mouth an' laughs.⑧

---

① Blues：一种感伤的美国黑人民歌，又指慢四步爵士舞曲。
② De："The"的误读，还有后面的 I wants 等，都是模拟未受教育的黑人所讲的英语。
③ Ever'：Every 之讹。
④ Ma heart was in ma mouth：Ma 是 My 的误读；按习语 have one's heart in one's mouth 是"非常惊讶"或"焦急万分"之意。

怀乡布鲁斯

铁路上的桥
是空中的悲唱。
铁路上的桥
是空中的悲唱。
每回火车过
我就想搭上。

我去过车站；
心跳到喉咙口。
我去过车站；
心跳到喉咙口。
想找辆棚车
载我往南走。

怀乡布鲁斯，
上帝呀，这真糟。
怀乡布鲁斯，
怀上了就太糟。
我怕哭出来，
只得张口笑。

---

⑤ box car：棚车，美国英语。

⑥ Lawd = Lord，主，称呼上帝。

⑦ 'S = Is，它的主语 blues 是单数名词。

⑧ an' = and.

A BLACK MAN TALKS OF REAPING

I have sown beside all waters in my day.
I planted deep, within my heart the fear[①]
That wind or fowl would take the grain away.
I planted safe against this stark, lean year.

I scattered seed enough to plant the land[②]
In rows from Canada to Mexico
But for my reaping only what the hand
Can hold at once is all that I can show.[③]

Yet what I sowed and what the orchard yields
My brother's sons are gathering stalk and root,[④]
Small wonder then my children glean in fields[⑤]
They have not sown, and feed on bitter fruit.[⑥]

---

①   within my heart the fear = within my heart there being the fear,或 = with the fear within my heart.

②   seed：单数形式是"种子"的统称＝seeds。

③   at once：这里作"一次地"解，也即"一把"。

④   stalk and root：连梗带根，作状语，修饰 are gathering，不是 are gathering 的宾语，宾语是 what I sowed and what the orchard yields。

黑人谈收获

年轻时我曾在一切岸边播种子。
我种得很深,因为我心中在担忧,
怕种子被风儿吹走或被鸟啄食。
我种得很稳,为了防这荒年歉收。

我撒的种子足以在北起加拿大、
南到墨西哥的土地上进行条播,
但说到收成,只有我的手能一把
握住的,才是可出示的全部所获。

然而我种的庄稼和果园的出产,
我兄弟的儿子们连梗带根收去.
我的孩子在他们没播种的田间
拾落穗,靠烂果充饥就不足为奇。

---

⑤ Small wonder:也作 No wonder 或 Little wonder,无怪,是习语,后面有时用连词 that。

⑥ fields / They have not sown:They 前面省略 that 或 which;sow,播种,这里它的宾语是"土地"。

FOUR GLIMPSES OF NIGHT

1

Eagerly

Like a woman hurrying to her lover

Night comes to the room of the world

And lies, yielding and content

Against the cool round face

Of the moon.

2

Night is a curious child, wandering

Between earth and sky, creeping

In windows and doors, daubing

The entire neighborhood

With purple paint.

Day

Is an apologetic mother

Cloth in hand[1]

Following after.

---

[1] Cloth in hand = with cloth in hand.

对夜色的四瞥

一

像个女子
满怀热望地赶来会情人
夜来到世界的房间里
躺下，顺从而又心满意足地
贴着月儿的
凉凉圆脸。

二

夜是个古怪的孩子
漫游在天地之间，
他溜进门窗，用紫色的漆
把整个这一带
乱涂一气。
白天
是带着歉意的母亲
手中拿着抹布
跟在后面。

3

Peddling
From door to door
Night sells
Black bags of peppermint stars[2]
Heaping cones of vanilla moon[3]
Until
His wares are gone
Then shuffles homeward
Jingling the gray coins
Of daybreak.

4

Night's brittle song, silver-thin
Shatters into a billion fragments
Of quiet shadows
At the blaring jazz
Of a morning sun.

---

② peppermint stars：星有凉意，故称"薄荷星星"。

三

挨门挨户地
兜售
夜卖着
一些黑口袋装着的薄荷星星
堆得满满的香草月亮蛋筒
直到
他货儿无存
才一步一拖地走回家
把黎明的灰色硬币
弄得丁当响。

四

脆薄的夜色银歌
碎成亿万块的
宁静影子的碎片
因为听见了
响得刺耳的朝阳爵士乐。

---

③ cones of vanilla moon：装香草月亮的蛋筒，比较李清照词中有"双溪舴艋舟载不动许多愁"，一个是小舟载忧愁，一个是蛋筒装月亮，实乃古今中外异曲同工的绝妙奇想。

THE MEADOW MOUSE[①]

1

In a shoe box stuffed in an old nylon stocking
Sleeps the baby mouse I found in the meadow,
Where he trembled and shook beneath a stick
Till I caught him up by the tail and brought him in,
Cradled in my hand,[②]
A little quaker, the whole body of him trembling,[③]
His absurd whiskers sticking out like a cartoon-mouse,
His feet like small leaves,
Little lizard-feet,
Whitish and spread wide when he tried to struggle away,
Wriggling like a miniscule puppy.

Now he's eaten his three kinds of cheese and drunk from
       his bottle-cap watering-trough—
So much he just lies in one corner,[④]
His tail curled under him, his belly big
As his head; his batlike ears
Twitching, tilting toward the least sound.

Do I imagine he no longer trembles
When I come close to him?
He seems no longer to tremble.

---

① Meadow mouse：田鼠，也称 field mouse。
② Cradled：过去分词，把……放在摇篮里，这里用摇篮比喻手掌。

田　鼠

一

被塞进一只旧尼龙长丝袜的鞋盒里
睡着我在草场上捉来的一只幼鼠：
发现时它在一根枯枝下抖抖瑟瑟，
直到我拎住它尾巴并带着它回家；
这打颤的小东西
蜷缩在我手中，整个的身子抖个不停，
它可笑的胡子像卡通里的老鼠那样戳出着，
它的几只脚像略显白色的小叶子，
像很小四脚蛇的脚，
当它想挣扎着跑掉时这些脚趴得很开，
而全身蠕动着像一头极小的狗。

现在它已吃了三种干酪，又从权充水盂的瓶盖里
　　喝了水——
这一顿吃喝撑得它只好躺在鞋盒的角落里，
尾巴弯曲在身下，肚子大得
像它的脑袋；只要听见一点点声音
就会抽动和侧起它那蝙蝠似的耳朵。

我可是在猜想当我走近它时
它已经不再颤抖？
它看来是不再颤抖了。

---

③　A little quaker：是前面 him（即 the baby mouse）的同位语。

④　So much：后面省略 that，吃喝得那么多，以至……。

2

But this morning the shoe box house on the back porch is
     empty.
Where has he gone, my meadow mouse,
My thumb of a child that nuzzled in my palm? —⑤
To run under the hawk's wing,
Under the eye of the great owl watching from the elm tree,
To live by courtesy of the shrike, the snake, the tomcat.

I think of the nestling fallen into the deep grass,
The turtle gasping in the dusty rubble of the highway,
The paralytic stunned in the tub, and the water rising—⑥
All things innocent, hapless, forsaken.

---

⑤　My thumb of a child：我们拇指般（大小）的孩子；这是由"a...of a..."构成的习语
　　形式，如 a gem of a poem，宝石般（精美）的诗，his angel of a wife，他的天使般的妻
　　子。

二

但是在今天早晨，放在后门廊的那个鞋盒住宅
　　里已空空如也。
它去了哪里，我那田鼠，
那蜷卧在我手掌里的拇指般大的孩子？——
是去在鹰隼的翅膀下奔逃，
在榆树上巨大猫头鹰的眈眈俯视下，
凭伯劳、蛇和大雄猫的宽大而生存。

我想到掉落在深深草丛里的雏鸟，
在大路上尘土覆盖的碎石里喘气的海龟，
在水渐渐涨起的澡盆里因中风而昏厥的人——
那些没有罪过、孤苦无援的不幸万物。

---

⑥　stunned：过去分词，修饰名词 the paralytic。

NOSTALGIA

My soul stands at the window of my room,
    And I ten thousand miles away;[①]
My days are filled with Ocean's sound of doom,
    Salt and cloud and the bitter spray.
Let the wind blow, for many a man shall die.

My selfish youth, my books with gilded edge,
    Knowledge and all gaze down the street;[②]
The potted plants upon the window ledge
    Gaze down with selfish lives and sweet,[③]
Let the wind blow, for many a man shall die.

My night is now her day, my day her night,
    So I lie down, and so I rise;
The sun burns close, the star is losing height,[④]
    The clock is hunted down the skies.
Let the wind blow, for many a man shall die.

---

① I:后面省略 am。

② and all:等等,是习语。

③ selfish lives and sweet = selfish and sweet lives.

怀 乡 思 旧

我房间的窗前站着我的灵魂，
　　而我人却在一万英里外；
我日子充满大洋的死亡之声、
　　苦涩的浪花、盐花和云霭。
　　让风吹吧，因为多少人得死亡。

我自私的青春、烫金的书、知识
　　和一切，凝神俯视着街上；
盆栽植物的生命甜美而自私，
　　也都在窗台上朝下凝望。
　　让风吹吧，因为多少人得死亡。

如今，我的昼夜同她的正交错，
　　所以我无奈地躺下、起身；
太阳贴近着燃烧，它正在降落，
　　天上这钟被追踪到西沉。
　　让风吹吧，因为多少人得死亡。

④　the star：在诗中常指北极星，如莎士比亚十四行诗集第 116 首第 7 行［love］is the
　　star to every wandering bark；但此处似指前面的 The sun，而且下一行的 The
　　clock 似乎也指 The sun。本诗写于 1942 年 3 月，当时诗人是参战的军人，正在印度
　　洋上，此刻目送太阳渐渐西沉，更引起他思念在西方的家乡。

Truly a pin can make the memory bleed,

   A world explode the inward mind[5]

And turn the skulls and flowers never freed

   Into the air, no longer blind.[6]

Let the wind blow, for many a man shall die.

Laughter and grief join hands. Always the heart

   Clumps in the breast with heavy stride;

The face grows lined and wrinkled like a chart,

   The eyes bloodshot with tears and tide.

Let the wind blow, for many a man shall die.

---

[5] A world explode: 承前，= A world can explode.

真的，一根针能扎得记忆流血，
　　一个世界能炸开人内心，
能使从不自由的花朵和脑子
　　就此睁开了眼、进入天空。
让风吹吧，因为多少人得死亡。

欢笑和悲伤手拉着手，胸膛里
　　总感到心的沉重大跨步；
脸变得像航图，纹路又加皱襞，
　　泪和潮使眼中血丝密布。
让风吹吧，因为多少人得死亡。

⑥　no longer blind：不再是盲目的，也就是这才认识战争的祸患。

MANHOLE COVERS

The beauty of manhole covers—what of that?[1]
Like medals struck by a great savage kahn,
Like Mayan calendar stones, unliftable, indecipherable,[2]
Not like old electrum, chased and scored,
Mottoed and sculptured to a turn,[3]
But notched and whelked and pocked and smashed
With the great company names:
Gentle Bethlehem, smiling United States.
This rustproof artifact of my street,
Long after roads are melted away, will lie
Sidewise in the grave of the iron-old world,[4]
Bitten at the edges,
Strong with its cryptic American,
Its dated beauty.[5]

---

[1] what of that?：口语，也常作 what of it? 意思是"那又怎么样呢?"或者"有什么了不起呢？"

[2] Mayan ['mɑːjən] calendar stones：马雅历法碑；马雅历是古代中美洲历法，马雅人树石碑(厚石块或石柱)，在碑上镌刻象征性的图画和统治者生活中的重要日期和事件。

窨 井 盖

窨井盖的那种美——那又怎样？
像一位凶猛大汗铸就的勋章，
像难懂又移不动的马雅历法碑，
不像刻过或矻过的古代银金
没有恰到好处的格言或雕刻，
只是被凿、被扭、被敲打出来
几个大公司麻麻点点的名称：
温和的伯利恒、盈盈微笑的合众国。
我街上这种防锈的工艺制品
在道路融化之后很久，将歪斜在
铁器时代的古墓里——
边缘已经锈蚀，
富于神秘的亚美利加风格，
富于古老的美。

---

③　to a turn：恰到好处，尽善尽美地，是习语。
④　Sidewise ＝ Sideways，斜侧，靠在一边，副词，有时也作形容词。
⑤　dated：古旧的。

BALLAD OF BIRMINGHAM[①]

(On the bombing of a church in Birmingham, Alabama, 1963)

"Mother dear, may I go downtown
instead of out to play,
and march the streets of Birmingham
in a Freedom March today? "

"No, baby, no, you may not go,[②]
for the dogs are fierce and wild,
and clubs and hoses, guns and jails
ain't good for a little child. "[③]

"But, mother, I won't be alone.
Other children will go with me,
and march the streets of Birmingham
to make our country free. "

"No, baby, no, you may not go,
for I fear those guns will fire.
But you may go to church instead,
and sing in the children's choir. "

---

① Birmingham['bə:miŋhæm]:伯明翰,美国亚拉巴马州城市,Ballad 是英语诗歌中的
一种传统形式,每节多为四行,奇数行四音步,偶数行三音步,且押韵。

伯明翰歌谣

（为 1963 年亚拉巴马州伯明翰市
的教堂爆炸事件而作）

　　"亲爱的妈妈，我不想去玩；
　　　你可让我去市中心
　　参加伯明翰街上的游行？
　　　今天有'向自由进军'。"

　　"不行，宝贝，不行，你别去，
　　　因为狗东西太狂暴；
　　棍棒和水龙、枪子和牢房，
　　　对于小孩子可不好。"

　　"妈妈，那儿不是我一个人。
　　　别人家孩子也都去——
　　参加伯明翰街上的游行，
　　　为国家把自由争取。"

　　"不行，宝贝，不行，你别去，
　　　因为我担心会开枪。
　　我说你就去儿童唱诗班，
　　　去教堂里一起唱唱。"

---

② baby：[美口]姑娘。

③ ain't [eint]：[口]＝ are not, am not, is not，俚语中还 ＝ have not, has not。

She has combed and brushed her nightdark hair,
and bathed rose petal sweet,[④]
and drawn white gloves on her small brown hands,
and white shoes on her feet.

The mother smiled to know her child
was in the sacred place,[⑤]
but that smile was the last smile
to come upon her face.

For when she heard the explosion,
her eyes grew wet and wild.
She raced through the streets of Birmingham
calling for her child.

She clawed through bits of glass and brick,
then lifted out a shoe.
"O, here's the shoe my baby wore,
but, baby, where are you? "

---

④ bathed rose petal sweet：洗得玫瑰花般地芳香；rose petal 起状语作用，修饰表语
sweet。

她把乌黑的头发梳又刷，
　　擦洗得玫瑰般芬芳；
棕色的小手戴上白手套，
　　脚上穿白皮鞋一双。

想到孩子去神圣的教堂，
　　做母亲的露出微笑；
但是这微笑在她的脸上
　　此后就再也看不到。

因为当她听到了爆炸声，
　　她眼光慌乱眼眶湿，
急急奔过伯明翰的街道，
　　一面在呼叫她孩子。

她在断砖碎玻璃间扒拉，
　　接着把一只鞋抓起。
"哦，这就是我宝贝穿的鞋，
　　可宝贝呀你在哪里？"

⑤　sacred place：神圣的地方，指教堂。

TO SATCH^①

Sometimes I feel like I will *never* stop^②

Just go on forever

'Til one fine mornin'^③

I'm gonna reach up and grab me a handfulla stars^④

Swing out my long lean leg

And whip three hot strikes burnin' down the heavens^⑤

And look over at God and say

How about that!^⑥

---

① Satch：即 Satchel Paige（1906？—1982），美国职业棒球投手，球龄特长，号称铁人，以幽默及善投变速球著称。虽因黑人而受种族歧视，还是在 1971 年选入美国棒球荣誉厅。

② feel like：[口] 想要，通常后面跟名词或动名词，这里后面跟名词从句，似较特殊。

致 萨 切

有时候我巴望我永远不会停下

只管不断地干下去

直干到一个大好的早晨

那时我抬手抓它一大把星星

跷起我细长的腿一甩

趁势猛投三个好球灭老天威风

随后抬眼看着上帝对他说

这下怎么样！

---

③ 'Til = Until. mornin'：morning 的误读，后面的 burnin' 同。

④ gonna：[美俚]＝going to. grab me ＝ grab for me ＝ grab for myself. a handfulla ＝ a handful of.

⑤ strike：棒球赛中投手所投的好球，也指对所投球的迎击。

⑥ How about...！：……怎么样！

MUSEUM PIECE

The good gray guardians of art
Patrol the halls on spongy shoes,
Impartially protective, though
Perhaps suspicious of Toulouse.[①]

Here dozes one against the wall,
Disposed upon a funeral chair.
A Degas dancer pirouettes[②]
Upon the parting of his hair.

See how she spins! The grace is there,
But strain as well is plain to see.[③]
Degas loved the two together:
Beauty joined to energy.[④]

Edgar Degas purchased once
A fine El Greco, which he kept[⑤]
Against the wall beside his bed
To hang his pants on while he slept.[⑥]

---

① suspicious of Toulouse[tu(:) 'luːz]：对 Toulouse 的画的艺术价值感到怀疑；
Henri de Toulouse-Lautree，法国画家。

② Degas [də'gɑː]：德加，法国画家。pirouettes[piru'ets]：芭蕾舞中用脚尖立地旋转。

③ strain as well = strain as well as the grace.

美 术 珍 品

这些白发的艺术好看守·
脚穿软底鞋巡视着展厅，
他们的保护不偏心，尽管
对于土鲁斯也许有疑心。

这儿有一位靠着墙打盹，
坐在办丧事用的椅子里。
在他头路上踮着脚转的
是位德加画的芭蕾舞女。

瞧她那旋转是多么优美！
但拼力使劲也同样明显，
德加爱的是这两者结合：
是要在力量中把美包含。

埃德加·德加买过一张
艾尔·格列柯很好的画，
他把画靠在床边的墙上——
睡觉时裤子往画上一挂。

---

④　joined：过去分词；Beauty joined to energy，说明上行的 the two together。

⑤　El Greco[el′grekəu]：艾尔·格列柯，西班牙画家。

⑥　hang his pants on while he slept：睡眠时把裤子挂在 El Greco 的画上，自有鄙夷之意，当是嫌其奔放有余，精细不足。

400-METER FREESTYLE

THE GUN full swing the swimmer catapults and cracks[①]

s
i
x[②]

feet away onto that perfect glass he catches at

a
n
d

throws behind him scoop after scoop cunningly moving[③]

t
h
e

water back to move him forward. Thrift is his wonderful

s
e
c

ret; he has schooled out all extravagance. No muscle[④]

r
i
p[⑤]

ples without compensation wrist cock to heel snap to

h
i
s

mobile mouth that siphons in the air that nurtures[⑥]

h
i
m

---

① 本诗形式特殊,每行末用三个字母和下一行连接,形象地表现了游泳者在池边的转身来回;译文更好,每行用一字和下行连接,并利用方块字的先天特点,一行顺排,一行倒排,更加活现了游泳者在水中来回游泳的景象。full swing = in full swing,完全自由地,十分活跃地。catapults [ˈkætəpʌlts]:原为名词,指"发射器",这里是动词,谓似用发射器推动着迅猛跃出。cracks:砰然着水。

400 米自由泳

枪响游泳者猛一跃扑到整整六尺外
　　　　　　　　　　溅
后推前插手的他上面水的镜如到落
熟
练地把水一下一下往后甩为的是让
　　　　　　　　　　　他
他；算细打精是诀秘妙奇的他。进前
练
得没一点浪费。凡肌肉的细微运动
　　　　　　　　　　都
到水打跟脚到曲弯腕手从，偿报有
灵
活吸气的嘴，可以说那滋养他的空
　　　　　　　　　气

---

② perfect glass：指水面如镜，它后面不用句号而紧接下句，象征游泳者气也不换，飞速前进。

③ scoop after scoop：如一勺一勺舀水似地一划一划，是 catches at 和 throws 的宾语。

④ has schooled out all extravagance：练成不浪费一分气力的工夫。

⑤ wrist cock：前面省略 from。

⑥ siphons in the air：吸入空气；siphon，原义"虹吸"，这里就是"吸"；in 是副词。

at half an inch above the sea level so to speak . ⑦
T
he

astonishing whites of the soles of his feet rise
a
n
d

salute us on the turns. He flips, converts, and is gone ⑧
a
l
l

in one. We watch him for signs. His arms are steady at
t
h
e

catch, his cadent feet tick in the stretch, they know
t
h
e

lesson well. Lungs know . too; he does not list for ⑨
a
i
r

he drives along on little sips carefully expended
b
u
t

that plum red heart pumps hard cries hurt how soon ⑩
i
t
s

near one more and makes its final surge TIME : 4 : 2 5 : 9 ⑪

---

⑦ at half an inch above the sea level：按海平面下不适合人的生存。so to speak：可以
这样说，比方这样说，用作插入语。

⑧ on the turns：在游泳池两端转身的时候；flips, converts, and is gone all in one：all
in one，全在一起，这里是说几个动作在一个动作里完成。

　　　　人令的他时头掉。寸半仅面平海离
惊

　　　　奇的白脚底起来招呼我们。他一个
　　　　　　　　　　　　　　　　　滚

　　　　他着待等们我。去而游急头转掉翻
出

　　　　现征兆。他手臂划水稳健两脚有节
　　　　　　　　　　　　　　　　　奏

　　　　他；样一也肺。能其显各水打路一地
并

　　　　不侧身吸气，他前进是凭节约使用
　　　　　　　　　　　　　　　　　小

　　　　心雄色红梅的血泵力努但气吸的口
在

　　　　高喊受不了。还要多久？已经近啦
　　　　　　　　　　　　　　　　　再

　　　4分25秒9 间时搏一后最是便下一

---

⑨　list：侧转。

⑩　pumps hard cries hurt：可理解为 pumps hard (and) cries："（I [the heart] am) hurt！"

⑪　how soon its near one more and makes its final surge ＝ How soon it's (it [终点] is) near! One more surge and it (如泵的心脏) makes its final surge.

CLOSE-UP

Are all these stones
      yours
I said
and the mountain[①]
pleased

but reluctant to
admit my praise could move it much

shook a little
and rained a windrow ring of stones[②]
to show
that it was so[③]

Stonefelled I got[④]
up addled with dust[⑤]

and shook
      myself
without much consequence

---

①   the mountain：它的谓语动词是第 3 节开首的 shook，中间是插入的修饰语。
②   rained a windrow ring of stones：rained，像雨一样落下；windrow，风吹拢的一堆（灰土、树叶等）。

接　近

所有这些石头都是
　　你的吗
我说
于是大山
高兴了

但不愿承认
我这夸赞能使它大为感动

就稍稍一抖
便下了一圈石雨
以此表明
它是这情况

被石头击倒的我
呛够了灰尘胡乱爬起

也把自己
　　一抖
却没什么结果

---

③　it was so：它就是这个样子的。

④　Stonefelled ＝ Felled by the stones.

⑤　dust：统称"尘土"，没有复数；a dust 是"一阵尘土"。

Obviously I said it doesn't pay[⑥]
to get too
close up to
          greatness
and the mountain friendless wept
          and said
it couldn't help[⑦]
itself

---

⑥ pay：值得。

我说很明显同
　　　伟大
太接近
并不值得
于是断了亲友的大山
　　　哭着说
它可由不得
自己

⑦　这两行意为：它无可奈何，不由自主，即第 3 节所说的"它就是这个样子的"。它伟大，所以你不能太靠近它，靠近了，它石块乱飞，非打击你不可。

A CHRISTMAS TREE①

Star,②

If you are

A love compassionate,

You will walk with us this year.③

We face a glacial distance, who are here④

Huddld⑤

At your feet.

---

① 本诗是一首押韵的诗,吟咏的内容是圣诞树,形式也是一棵圣诞树。

② Star:司命星,如 be born under a lucky(或 unlucky, ill) star,转义为"好运气",如 be through with one's star (好运过去了)。把 Star 放在顶上也有像形作用,因为圣诞树的顶上,人们常饰一星。

③ this year:指从这个圣诞节起到下个圣诞节的这一年。

圣 诞 树

星啊，

你那爱中

如果含有怜悯，

来年就和我们同行。

这里我们面对冰河距离

拥挤

在你脚底。

---

④ glacial distance：distance 原有"疏远、冷淡"之意，再饰以 glacial，更使人感到时间上之远和"冷若冰川（glacier）"。

⑤ Huddld：应是 Huddled，拥挤，这里故意漏拼一个字母，使这个词给人看了便觉得拥挤，译文用繁体的"拥挤"，正好取得同样的效果。

MIRROR

I am silver and exact. I have no preconceptions.

Whatever I see I swallow immediately

Just as it is, unmisted by love or dislike.

I am not cruel, only truthful—

The eye of a little god, four-cornered.

Most of the time I meditate on the opposite wall.

It is pink, with speckles. I have looked at it so long

I think it is a part of my heart. But it flickers. ①

Faces and darkness separate us over and over. ②

Now I am a lake. A woman bends over me,

Searching my reaches for what she really is.

Then she turns to those liars, the candles or the moon.

I see her back, and reflect it faithfully.

She rewards me with tears and an agitation of hands.

I am important to her. She comes and goes.

Each morning it is her face that replaces the darkness.

In me she has drowned a young girl, and in me an old
   woman③

Rises toward her day after day, like a terrible fish. ④

---

① I think: 前面省略 That。

② over and over: 也作 over and over again, 一再, 反复, 是习语。

镜

我是银的，是一丝不苟的。我没有成见。
我无论看见什么，就立刻原封不动地
接受下来，不会因喜爱或讨厌而迷惘。
我并不残酷，只是忠实而已——
是位小小天神的眼睛，四角方方。
多半的时间，我总朝着对面的墙默想。
它粉红色，有着斑点。我久久望着它，
便以为是我心的一部分。但它时明时暗。
一些面庞和黑暗一次次把我们隔开。

现在我是湖水。一个女人俯身朝着我，
细细察看我所能反映的她的真实面貌。
接着，她求助于总是撒谎的蜡烛或月光。
我看见她的后背，就忠实地反映出来。
她给我的报答，是泪水和手的颤动。
我对她很重要。她在我跟前来来去去。
每天早晨，总是她的脸来接替黑暗。
我这里，她溺毙个少女；我这里，有个老妇
逐日起来迎向她，像条可怕的鱼。

③ In me she has drowned a young girl：她在我这湖里（即镜子里）溺毙了一个少女（即
她自己的少女形象，也即她的少女时代的容貌已经消失了）。
④ fish：用 fish 称人原有贬意，如 a queer fish，怪人；这里说她已成 a terrible fish，其
可悲的丑陋形象可以想见。

作 者 简 介

Anne Bradstreet　（1612—1672）

生于英国有文化教养的清教徒家庭。十六岁结婚,1630 年全家迁至马萨诸塞殖民地。她虽子女众多,但写诗不辍。她的姐夫未经她同意,把她的一些手稿带到英国出版,书名为《新近在美洲出现的第十位缪斯》。这本书虽使作者大感意外,却是新大陆诗人的第一部诗集。而她的宗教组诗《沉思集》则被二十世纪文学批评界视为不朽之作。《作者致自己的诗集》一诗以当时流行的英雄偶句体写成。这种诗体的特点是每行含五个抑扬格音步(十音节),每两行押一韵。

Edward Taylor　（1645—1729）

生于英国农家,因不愿效忠于英国国教而移居新英格兰。在哈佛大学肄业三年后任牧师和医师。他生前未发表诗,本世纪三十年代,其多为宗教题材的诗稿在耶鲁大学发现,被认为继承了英国玄学派诗歌的特点,意象奇特,比喻出人意表,达到了清教徒文学的最高峰。

Philip Freneau　（1752—1832）

生于纽约,毕业于普林斯顿大学。美国革命爆发后开始创作反英作品,并因从加勒比地区回国参战而不幸被俘。此后当过船长并重新进入新闻界,写诗热烈拥护革命。这些经历使他赢得了"美国诗歌之父"及"美国独立革命的诗人"等称号。他对英诗传统及新古典主义作品颇有素养,《义勇军进行曲》一诗的第二、三、四、六、七节与苏格兰诗人彭斯的名作《苏格兰同袍》相当接近,其它诗节中的一些词语也取自该诗(可参看上海译文版《英国抒情诗选》)。

William Cullen Bryant　（1794—1878）

生于马萨诸塞州一医生家庭,是早期清教徒移民之后。曾在大学肄业一年并当了近十年律师。1821 年出版第一本《诗集》后被视为诗坛新秀。后移居纽约,任报纸主笔近五十年。他热爱大自然,很受英国诗人华兹华斯(1770—1850）的影响,是美国的第一位浪漫主义诗人,也是第一位赢得国际声誉的美国作家。在政治上他痛恨奴隶制,积极拥护林肯。

George Moses Horton　（1797?—1883?）

　　生于北卡罗来纳州一农场的黑人奴隶,颇有诗歌天赋,还不会读书写字时已能即兴吟诗,曾打算以作诗所得为自己赎身。1829 年出版了一本由他人笔录的诗集《希望自由》。其它作品有《赤裸的天才》等。

Ralph Waldo Emerson　（1803—1882）

　　生于波士顿一教士家庭,哈佛神学院毕业后一度教书及当牧师。对自己的信仰产生怀疑而脱离教会后赴欧,会见了华兹华斯、柯尔律治等英国诗人,深受欧洲浪漫主义运动影响。回美国后开始介绍他的超验主义理论,宣告美国文学已脱离英国文学而独立。所有这些以及他的作品,使他不仅成为重要的美国诗人及美国文艺复兴(1835—1865）的领袖,而且是欧洲浪漫主义潮流在美国的代言人,对当时及后代的作家影响巨大。而在南北战争爆发时,他支持林肯政府,主张废除奴隶制。

Henry Wadsworth Longfellow　（1807—1882）

　　缅因州人,在学期间语言才能突出,毕业后被母校鲍登学院聘为近代语言教授,并按规定先去欧洲学习法、意及西班牙语,成为美国当时少数现代语言教授之一。此后受聘于哈佛大学,又去了德、英、瑞典、荷兰等国。1836 年起在哈佛任教授,介绍欧洲文化;1854 年辞去教职,潜心写作。他的作品通俗自然、铿锵流畅,是生前最受美英读者欢迎的美国诗人。

John Greenleaf Whittier　（1807—1892）

　　生于贫苦的清教徒农家,仅受过有限的正规教育,但一直热爱华兹华斯、柯尔律治等英国诗人的作品,并很早开始写作。他青年时代即入报界,1845—1860 年间,是连载了《汤姆大伯的小屋》的刊物《国民时代》的编辑。他的作品使他成为废奴运动的杰出人物和重要作家,在美英两国同朗费罗一样家喻户晓。

Edgar Allan Poe （1809—1849）

生于波士顿一演员家庭，母死后由教父爱伦收养，带到英国后受到很好的教育。1826 年返美后入弗吉尼亚大学肄业一年，学习了希腊、拉丁、法、意、西班牙等语。后曾短期在西点军校任职并当过编辑。他作品多种多样，既写文艺评论，又擅长推理小说和恐怖小说，诗作则深受英国诗歌影响，强调用词、格律与结构，在音韵上颇有创新。

Oliver Wendell Holmes （1809—1894）

生于马萨诸塞州一绅士家庭。在哈佛大学学习法律时是年级诗人。后去法国学医，1836 年为哈佛大学医学博士，开业十年后进达特默斯学院教授过解剖学，此后曾任哈佛大学医学院院长。但他更以其文学作品而知名于世，被认为是幽默作家和诗人。他倾向于十八世纪的文学趣味，写的诗以轻快俏皮或巧妙优雅见胜。

Jones Very （1813—1880）

生于马萨诸塞州，哈佛大学毕业后当了牧师，但只偶然讲道。因精神异常曾进医院治疗，出院后长期过着与世隔绝的生活。他写散文也写诗，诗中常有宗教气息，可使人联想到十七世纪英国玄学派诗人的宗教诗。爱默生称他为"果敢的圣人"。

James Russell Lowell （1819—1891）

生于马萨诸塞州波士顿名门。1840 年在哈佛大学毕业前曾是年级诗人。1844 年结婚后，受妻子影响积极投入废奴运动并大力创作，1848 年发表代表作《比格罗诗稿》。1855 继朗费罗在哈佛大学教授了二十年的欧洲文学。1857 年起曾编辑过著名刊物《大西洋月刊》和《北美评论》多年，是"优雅传统"的评论家代表。晚年曾两度以使节身分驻欧，在英期间曾任华兹华斯学会主席。

Walt Whitman （1819—1892）

生于纽约长岛。11 岁因家贫辍学后便外出谋生，从事过多种职业，后进报馆，终成编辑。南北战争时主动去华盛顿护理伤员，中年以后经济渐窘迫。他的代表作《草叶集》于 1855 年初版后，褒贬纷纭，但确立了与传统诗歌迥异的风格：诗句近似口语，不押韵，不计音步，重音的出现不规则，诗行及诗节的长短不拘。他的作品实现了他要在诗中将自由、民主的普通人和粗犷、豪放的个人相结合的理想,对美国文化的发展有重大影响。

Julia Ward Howe　(1819—1910)

生于纽约,母家姓 Ward。1843 年与社会改革家、盲人学校教师 S. G. Howe 结婚后,曾一起编辑《共和报》,致力于废除奴隶制及争取妇女权利。她写有游记、传记、童谣及诗集多卷,但留芳至今乃凭本书所选的这首《共和国战歌》。

Frederick Goddard Tuckerman　(1821—1873)

生于波士顿,毕业于哈佛大学。1844 年取得律师资格,1847 年起潜心进行文学活动及科学研究。生前只出过一本诗集。本世纪三十年代美国诗人韦特·宾纳(1881—1968)编出《特克曼十四行诗集》后,他的较大胆的诗风渐受注意。

George Henry Boker　(1823—1890)

生于费城的剧作家和诗人,曾当过驻土耳其和俄国的外交官。他的这首《给一名军人的挽歌》与后面两首题材相似的诗主旨有所不同,这也许同他的经历不无关系。

Emily Dickinson　(1830—1886)

生于马萨诸塞州阿默斯特一律师家庭,受严格的清教徒思想影响。曾在其祖父为创办人之一的阿默斯特学院及芒特·霍利约克女子学院求学,二十八岁起便隐居在家,写诗自娱。由于她生前绝少发表作品,因此诗句的编排和标点现未能完全确定。这些诗大多短小凝练,生动准确,富于暗示,与后起的意象派诗歌有共通之处;而在形式上,她虽常用抑扬格的四行节,但又较为自由,押韵上也常押相似韵。因此,她被认为是现代派诗歌的先驱和写抒情短诗的大师。

Bret Harte　(1836—1902)

生于纽约州,未受正规教育,十一岁时即发表诗歌。辗转各地后,1854 年移居加州,体验了矿区生活。1860 年在旧金山当记者时开始创作生涯,作品有地方色彩,为后来人才辈出的乡土派作家开辟了道路。1871 年他受美国东部一流文学杂志《大西洋月刊》之邀,辞去加州大学教授之职。1878 年作为外交官派驻欧洲后,在伦敦度过余生。他的诗轻松有趣,同样颇受欢迎。

Thomas Bailey Aldrich （1836—1907）

生于新罕布什尔州。十三岁辍学后在纽约当店员,不久即为各种报刊撰稿,1855 年出版第一部诗集。后在《大西洋月刊》任编辑十年。他的小说常有出人意外的结局,对短篇小说的发展颇有影响。最有名的作品是根据其童年生活写的《一个坏孩子的故事》。

Joaquin Miller （1837—1913）

是 Cincinnatus Hiner Miller 的笔名。他生于向西迁移的大篷车上,十二岁时又随家移居俄勒冈州(后有"俄勒冈的拜伦"之称),最后迁至加州。他曾生活在印第安人之中,经营过邮递业务,做过法官和报纸编辑。他的诗常热情歌颂西部的原始景物,颇受时人好评。

Sidney Lanier （1842—1881）

生于佐治亚州一富于音乐传统之家,从小写诗。十八岁时以全班第一的成绩毕业于奥格尔索普大学并留校任教。南北战争爆发后入南军当兵,但仍不忘学习外语及研究音乐,后因被俘及战后徒步走回南方,健康受到影响。1873 年获巴尔的摩乐团首席笛手之职,得以潜心钻研音乐与文学。1879 年进约翰斯·霍普金斯大学讲授英国文学,写出《英国诗话》。他的诗富于音乐美,是十九世纪下半叶美国南方诗坛的代表。

John Vance Cheney （1848—1922）

生于纽约州。1871—1875 年先后在佛蒙特州和马萨诸塞州学习法律。曾在纽约开业一年。1887—1909 年先后在旧金山与芝加哥图书馆工作。出版过多卷诗集。

Ella Wilcox （1850—1919）

生于威斯康星州,母家姓 Wheeler。据说十多岁时便爱好写作。毕业于威斯康星大学,二十二岁起出版诗集,一生诗作达四十卷左右。

Eugène Field （1850—1895）

生于密苏里州,曾就学于多所大学,但均未获学位。他的童谣及哲理、感伤歌谣曾有一定的名声。这里选译的《蓝孩儿》,看似写玩具与孩子的友情,实为痛悼爱子,是他流传最广的短诗之一。

Edwin Markham　（1852—1940）

生于俄勒冈州拓荒者家庭,自幼丧父,家境贫寒,在加州山间牧场长大。十八岁进加州师院,后当教师等。1899 年因所写的社会抗议诗《扶锄者》(可参看上海译文版《美国抒情诗选》)而闻名全美,自此遂专心写作和演讲。

Henry Van Dyke　（1852—1933）

生于宾夕法尼亚州。普林斯顿大学神学院毕业后,当过牧师、文学教授和驻荷兰公使。他的作品多种多样,文笔优雅,有维多利亚时代特色。

Lizette Woodworth Reese　（1856—1935）

生于马里兰州,一生大多在巴尔的摩市教书。1887 年开始出版诗集,显示出抒情的天赋。她的诗常以在农村度过的童年生活为基础,歌颂大自然,但摆脱了十九世纪后期常见的那种感伤情调,文字朴素简洁而有鲜明个性,预示了二十世纪的抒情风格,因而引人注目。

Harriet Monroe　（1860—1936）

生于芝加哥,曾在女修道院受教育,后在芝加哥报馆作评论员。在她的诗作得到当地人赏识后,于 1912 年创办《诗刊》并任主编。对"芝加哥文艺复兴"及现代诗的发展作出了巨大的贡献(可参看《美国抒情诗选·前言》)。

Albert Bigelow Paine　（1861—1937）

出生于马萨诸塞州的编辑与传记作家,也写过小说和诗歌。

Bliss Carman　（1861—1929）

生于加拿大,曾在牛津大学和哈佛大学就学。1889 年起定居美国,当过编辑和新闻工作者等,曾编过一本《牛津美国诗选》(1927年初版)。他与 Richard Hovey 合作写就的一本《漫游者的歌集》曾多次再版。

Richard Hovey （1864—1900）

生于伊利诺伊州。达特茅斯学院毕业后，当过神学家、演员、记者和哥伦比亚大学教授。他受到法国象征派影响，译过梅特林克的剧本。他的诗则情绪饱满高昂，常为生命的欢乐而高歌。除了与 Carman 合作的《漫游者的歌集》等作品外，还写有以爱国主义为主的诗集，晚年拟以亚瑟王的传说写长诗，不幸未竟而卒。

William Vaughn Moody （1869—1910）

生于印第安那州。1893 年哈佛大学毕业后，曾在母校及芝加哥大学执教并创作，作品有剧本和诗。他的诗集虽有显示才华的佳作，但由于用语艰深等原因而流传不广。但在本书所选诗中，他的反战态度和讽刺口吻看来还相当明显。

Edgar Lee Masters （1869—1950）

生于堪萨斯州的律师家庭，但在伊利诺伊州祖父的农场长大，曾在诺克斯学院学习。在芝加哥当律师多年后，转向文学。1912 年参加芝加哥新诗运动，1915 年他出版的《匙河集》被认为是美国文学的一块里程碑和"美国的人间喜剧"，使他一举成名。

Edwin Arlington Robinson （1869—1935）

生于缅因州，在哈佛大学肄业两年后当过小职员，因诗才受西奥多·罗斯福总统注意，遂得到较好的工作和写作条件。1910 年辞职后埋头创作，1916 年起确立了诗坛上的地位。他的诗既继承了新英格兰传统，又追求构思和意境的新奇，被认为是现代派诗歌的先行者，并对 Robert Frost 等诗人产生过重大影响。

Stephen Crane （1871—1900）

生于新泽西州牧师家庭，曾在神学院和军事学院学习五年，后在纽约当记者并从事创作，所写的一些小说对美国现实主义文学的发展颇有贡献。他写有两本主要诗集，其中一本的书名即为《战争很仁慈》（从此诗可看出其反战情绪）。这些自由诗中努力以具体的意象进行表现的手法，可视为二十世纪新诗运动的先声。

Paul Laurence Dunbar （1872—1906）

生于俄亥俄州代顿市，父母曾是奴隶。他是代顿中学唯一的黑人学生，主编过校刊。后以开电梯为生。他的诗集受当时美国文坛泰斗豪威尔斯(1837—1920)注意后,在其支持下终于成名,被公认为第一个有杰出成就的黑人诗人和专业作家。

Amy Lowell　(1874—1925)

生于波士顿名门,二十八岁起致力于诗歌创作,早期作品较正统。但后来游历了法、埃及、土耳其、希腊等国后,诗歌中富于异国情调。她是意象主义和自由诗运动的先锋,推动了二十世纪美国的新诗创作。作品中偏重视觉形象而较少感情流露。

Robert Frost　(1874—1963)

生于加州一知识型家庭,十岁时迁至母亲在新英格兰的老家。在哈佛大学肄业两年后,从事过多种职业。1912 年举家移居英国,顺利地出版了两本获好评的诗集。1915 年荣归故国后四次获普利策诗歌奖,被称为是“新英格兰的农民诗人”,晚年是美国非正式的桂冠诗人。他的诗处于传统诗歌与现代派诗歌的交替点,是唯一能在当代美国以写主题严肃的诗歌为生的人。

Trumbull Stickney　(1874—1904)

生于瑞士日内瓦,父亲是美国学者。他以优等成绩毕业于哈佛大学后,又成为第一个在巴黎大学获文学博士的美国人。归国后任哈佛大学的希腊语讲师,被认为是当时最有才学的人物之一。他的早亡使评论界深感惋惜,因为他与 W. V. Moody 被认为是极有前途的两位年轻诗人。

Carl Sandburg　(1878—1967)

生于伊利诺伊州一铁匠家庭,父亲为瑞典移民。十三岁起做过六年杂工。西美战争时在波多黎各当过志愿兵,战后免费入学,1902 年未得学位就离校,在各地从事多种职业。1912 年在《诗刊》上发表作品,1916 年出版《芝加哥诗集》,成了芝加哥诗派的重要人物,后又获得“普通人民的诗人”与“工业美国的诗人”名声。他的诗继承了 Whitman 与 Dickinson 的特点,形式自由而有节制,粗犷中见精细,豪放与婉约兼而有之。

Adelaide Crapsey　(1878—1914)

生于纽约州,1901 年瓦莎学院毕业后教历史与文学。1905 年去罗马研究考古学,回国后在斯密斯学院讲授诗学,因健康不佳,三年后即去世。这里所选的两首五行诗格律为其独创,各行的音节数为 2、4、6、8、2,看来受到日本俳句的影响。

Vachel Lindsay （1879—1931）

生于伊利诺伊州,曾在芝加哥艺术学院学美术。他虽属芝加哥诗派,但厌恶现代工业,曾徒步横贯美国,在各地吟诗诵歌二十多年,终因失望而自杀。他的诗节奏强烈独特,意象鲜明生动,被认为是新诗歌的代言人。

James Edward McCall （1880—?）

生于亚拉巴马州蒙哥马利市的黑人编辑和诗人。他原读医科,因突然罹疾失明而辍学,遂致力于文学。后在妹妹陪同下再度进大学学习,毕业后成为一受欢迎的报刊编辑(有妻子当助手)。

John Gneisenau Neihardt （1881—1973）

生于伊利诺伊州,在堪萨斯和内布拉斯加州长大,当过教师等。1901 到 1907 年生活在奥马哈印第安人之中,根据对他们习俗的研究和自己的体验创作。1921 年获内布拉斯加州桂冠诗人的称号,后在内布拉斯加大学任教授多年。

Edgar Albert Guest （1881—1959）

生于英国,十岁随家迁美。当过记者,后以日常生活为题材创作歌谣,颇受欢迎,以至于有些诗写成后,全美报纸一齐登载,从而家喻户晓。他的诗比较通俗幽默,轻松活泼,富于乐观情绪。

Marguerite Wilkinson （1883—1928）

生于加拿大新斯科舍省,曾在西北大学就学三年,写过包含宗教抒情诗在内的一些诗集并编过有一定影响的诗集。

William Carlos Williams （1883—1963）

生于新泽西州。宾夕法尼亚大学毕业,去莱比锡进修儿科后在故乡行医。他早期受意象主义影响,观察细致入微,笔调清澈明快,常取材于普通人民的生活并继承了 Whitman 的传统。一生写了三十多部诗文集,是现代美国诗坛的重要人物之一。

Sara Teasdale　(1884—1933)

生于密苏里州,学校毕业后曾游历欧洲和近东。1914 年嫁给一商人后迁居纽约,因性格不合等原因终于离异独居。她的抒情诗以朴素而甜美著名,但中年后常多悲声。她文笔精细纤巧,有较明显的古典风格。

Elinor Wylie　(1885—1928)

生于新泽西州,母家为费城名门,怀利是前夫的姓。自幼在首都就学和习画,后在纽约文艺界以诗才和美貌著称。1928 年重游英国即一病不起。其后夫 William Rose Benét(1886—1950,为后面 S. V. Benét 之兄)也是位诗人,为其编就出版了诗歌全集,轰动美国文坛。她的诗结构严谨,优美动听,实现了她"诗句要明快简洁,华美致密"的主张,但有时也流露一种孤傲高洁的贵族气。

Louis Untermeyer　(1885—1977)

生于纽约。中学时学业不佳,未毕业即随父经营珠宝业,但写诗不辍,1911 年开始出版诗集。三十八岁退职,去国外学习两年,回国后全力投入文学工作。五十岁前已编有《现代美国诗选》、《现代英国诗选》等三十多部诗文集,并曾为《不列颠百科全书》的美国现代诗部分撰写条目。

Ezra Pound　(1885—1972)

生于爱达荷州,就学于宾夕法尼亚大学,毕业前即掌握九种文字,1906 年获硕士学位,二十二岁获教授职。次年去欧洲,最后定居意大利。二次大战中因在罗马电台上抨击美国,战后遭美军逮捕,作为精神病患者拘禁于医院十二年后,获释去意大利。他二十五岁前出版的头两本诗集以韵律的新颖和内容的广博而受注目。1912 年在伦敦发起"意象主义运动",对现代英美诗歌的发展起了重大作用,并帮助推荐了一些文坛的后起之秀,如弗罗斯特和艾略特等。此外他还热衷于东方文化,在英美引起了研读东方古典作品的兴趣。

John Gould Fletcher　(1886—1950)

生于阿肯色州,哈佛大学毕业后在英国居留十多年,因诗风接近于强调诗歌音乐效果的意象派主张,后成为其主要人物之一。但二十年代起其诗风发生变化,作品不仅在形式上传统化起来,内容上的神秘主义倾向也加强了。回美后活跃于南方文坛,1950 年自尽。《林肯》一诗的原作共四章,各章相对独立,本书中选译的是其中最短小的第一章。

Hilda Doolittle （1886—1961）

生于宾夕法尼亚州,1904 年进大学,中途退学。1911 年游历意、法后在伦敦遇到 Pound,参加了意象派运动,为其重要代表之一,笔名 H. D. 。她恪守该派创作原则,以日常用语入诗,用词简洁而意象明确,却又透露出古典作品的影响。后期诗风转变,带神秘倾向。是二十世纪的重要诗人之一。

Georgia Douglas Johnson （1886—1966）

生于佐治亚州,母家姓 Camp。曾就学于亚特兰大大学等高校。1903 年嫁给从政的律师丈夫,随丈夫去华盛顿,在政府部门工作,是早期被公认为诗人的一位黑人妇女。

John Hall Wheelock （1886—1978）

生于长岛,毕业于哈佛大学,此后两年在德国著名的格丁根大学(十八世纪后期,该校是德国浪漫主义先驱诗人的中心)和柏林大学深造。他出版过《爱和解放》等诗集,以其年轻的歌声赞美生活,充满热情与活力,显然受 Whitman 和英国诗人 William Ernest Henley(可参看《英国抒情诗 100 首》、《英国抒情诗选》)的影响。

Marianne Moore （1887—1972）

生于密苏里州,在大学中主修生物学,毕业后又攻读商科。以后从事过多种职业,并成为刊物编辑和评论家。主要住在纽约。她的作品使她成为二十世纪二十年代的著名新诗人。这些诗常取材于大自然,观察细致,描写细腻,最后引出的结论有时虽较隐蔽,但富于真知灼见。作为诗人,她被认为发现了新题材和与之相适应的新结构、新体裁,开拓了诗的境界。

John Crowe Ransom （1888—1974）

生于田纳西州。在本州的范德比尔特大学毕业后又获牛津大学文学士学位。回国后,1914—1937 年在母校任教,其间因办诗刊《逃亡者》而形成诗派。此后在俄亥俄州的堪尼恩学院任教授,创办并主编重要的文艺评论刊物《堪尼恩评论》。1941 年发表《新批评》

一书,成了左右美国文学评论界的新批评派中心人物,并被选为美国文学艺术院院士。他的诗主要发表在三十年代之前,写得精密而有克制,以曲折的笔法表露了一种辛辣的幻灭感和幽默感。

Claude McKay （1890—1948）

生于牙买加一黑人家庭,当过木匠和警察。因其诗作有一定的战斗性,被迫离乡去美国。就学两年后来到纽约哈莱姆区,做过各种杂活。二十年代初登上文坛,参加编辑美共刊物。后思想渐趋消沉,1940 年成为美国公民。但他是以现实主义态度写城市黑人生活的第一位黑人诗人,是哈莱姆文艺复兴运动的先驱和杰出代表。

Edna St. Vincent Millay （1892—1950）

生于缅因州。1912 年发表的长诗《再生》被视为本世纪佳作之一。1917 年毕业于瓦莎女子学院后移居纽约,开始写作生涯并演出。她二十年代出版的几部诗集出色地写出当时浪漫女性的叛逆夸张气质,从而获得“女拜伦”等称号。此后她诗路开阔了一些,而由她撰写歌词的名歌剧《国王的心腹》,于 1927 年获得美国歌剧史上的空前成功。

Archibald MacLeish （1892—1982）

生于伊利诺伊州。耶鲁大学毕业后又在哈佛大学读法律。一次大战中赴法作战,回国后在波士顿当律师。1923 年携家赴法学习诗艺,在欧亚五年后返美,任《幸福》杂志编辑。三十年代又去西班牙作战。1939 至 1945 年任国会图书馆馆长,二次大战后为联合国教科文组织第一任主席。1949 年起任哈佛大学教授。他 1917 年开始出版诗集,后来则受到艾略特和庞德影响。1928 年回国后诗风转变,写出有社会内容的作品。

Maxwell Bodenheim （1893—1954）

生于密西西比州,十八岁参军,在军中完成了中学后继教育。后在芝加哥学过艺术和法律,但不久转向文学,1913 年在芝加哥文艺复兴中崭露头角,出版诗集和小说多种。他的意象派作品对美国诗歌的现代派运动有过贡献,并以独辟蹊径的诗风见称。

Elizabeth Coatsworth （1893—1986）

女诗人兼童话作家,从二十年代起出版了多部作品,常以色彩鲜明的形象处理一些东方题材。

e. e. cummings　（1894—1962）

生于马萨诸塞州。父亲是哈佛大学教授,他也毕业于该校。参加过第一次世界大战,写过十多部诗集、小说。他追求新奇的表现方法,采用市井的材料与语言,无视语法、标点符号的习惯,别出心裁地创造新字,连自己姓名的起首字母也不大写。评论界虽对他褒贬不一,但他对现代派诗歌的形式确有一定影响。

Jean Toomer　（1894—1967）

生于华盛顿,毕业于纽约大学,后在中学任教,不久转向写作,在黑人作家中有一定影响,但死后才被公认为著名作家。

Stephen Vincent Benet　（1898—1943）

出生于宾夕法尼亚一有文化修养的军人家庭。第一次世界大战中在政府里任文职,中断了在耶鲁大学的学习。一生写了十七部诗集与小说。早期作品中多美国题材的抒情诗。名作是以南北战争为背景的长诗《约翰·布朗的遗体》。其后的主要作品为一部对法西斯的威胁发出警告的《中午的梦魇》等。

Malcolm Cowley　（1898—1989）

生于宾夕法尼亚州,第一次世界大战时入伍,1900 年毕业于哈佛大学。在国外生活期间参加过左翼团体活动。后参与编辑重要刊物。因翻译法语文学作品,特别是诗歌和保尔·瓦莱利的作品而获文名。同时进行诗歌创作和文学评论,诗作主要是两卷写战后幻灭感的集子。

Leonie Adams　（1899—1988）

生于纽约市。大学时代即写诗,毕业后当过文学刊物编辑,后获奖学金出国游历两年,回国后执教于纽约大学,曾任国会图书馆诗歌顾问。由于作品中的技巧和神秘色彩,被称为现代的玄学派诗人。另外,她还翻译了法国诗人弗朗索瓦·维雍(1431—1465?)的作品。

Robert Francis　（1901—1987）

出生于宾夕法尼亚州。1923 年毕业于哈佛大学,1926 年获该校教育学硕士。1936年起出版了多部诗集,得到多次诗歌奖。

Theodore Spencer　(1902—1949)

出生于宾夕法尼亚州。普林斯顿大学毕业,1927年起在哈佛大学讲授英国文学,擅长于玄学派诗歌,发表过多部诗集及评论。

Langston Hughes　(1902—1967)

生于密苏里州,自幼父母分居。1923年自哥伦比亚大学辍学,当过水手,到过欧洲各地。回国当服务员时,将所写的三首诗放在前来就餐的 Vachel Lindsay 的餐具旁,得到赏识而被发现,不仅成为哈莱姆文艺复兴中最富才智的作家,也是最优秀的美国黑人诗人,最早把爵士乐、布鲁斯的节奏引入抒情诗,被称为"哈莱姆的桂冠诗人"。三十年代他曾访问前苏联和中国并去西班牙采访内战消息。后期创作转向小说和评论。

Arna Bontemps　(1902—1973)

出身于黑人家庭,父亲是砖瓦工,母亲是教师,在加州长大。完成大学教育后在纽约执教。作品有小说、传记、诗歌等,内容大多与黑人的历史和生活有关。

Frank Marshall Davis　(1905—1987)

黑人作家,做过教师、电台广播员、新闻工作者和编辑,曾出力帮助创立黑人报纸,并在四十年代讲授爵士音乐,但其诗名更著。

Theodore Roethke　(1908—1963)

生于密执安州一德国移民家庭。曾在密执安大学和哈佛大学学习,准备当律师。但获学位后决心以写诗为终生事业。1941年出版了第一本诗集。1948年起在华盛顿大学讲授诗学。他的诗诙谐机智,较为抒情。早期诗作受童年生活影响,多以自然景物为题材。本书所选《田鼠》一诗,即涉及动物、人与自然的关系。

Karl Shapiro　(1913—　)

生于巴尔的摩,曾就学于弗吉尼亚大学和约翰斯·霍普金斯大学,但因在校学习妨碍写作而退学。第二次大战时在海外服役,战后曾在约翰斯·霍普金斯及加州大学等处任教,编辑《诗刊》及担任国会图书馆诗歌顾问。他的诗题材广泛,既有强烈抒情,又有尖锐讽刺。本书所选的《窨井盖》则富于想象,从最普通的事物中发现美和不平凡。

Dudley Randall （1914— ）

生于华盛顿特区一黑人家庭。年轻时从事过多种职业,第二次世界大战时在海外服役,战后进密执安大学等,获硕士学位,曾在多处大学图书馆工作。1965 年办 Broadside Press,发表黑人诗人作品,1971 年编辑出版了《黑人诗人作品选》。本书中选择的作品,正如其标题所表明的,是一首以古老的传统形式写成的"歌谣",虽然其中有两行为取得特殊效果而"出格",基本上仍是四音步、三音步相间的格局。

Samuel Allen （1917— ）

生于俄亥俄州哥伦布市。曾先后在菲斯克、哈佛及巴黎大学学习。他的一些早期诗作受当时住在巴黎的美国著名黑人作家理查德·赖特赏识,而予以发表。1956 年在德国又以英、德两种文本出版诗集。有时用笔名 Paul Vesey,是位有一定知名度的黑人诗人。

Richard Wilbur （1921— ）

生于纽约一酒商家庭,自幼受家长鼓励写诗。大学毕业后入伍参战,战后写诗的态度趋于严肃。1950 年起在哈佛大学等高校讲授文学。他的抒情诗优美典雅,纤细精巧,而又不乏幽默,且讲究韵律,保持了某些诗歌传统。

Maxime Kumin （1925— ）

生于费城,曾在拉德克利夫学院就读。后在高校任教和独立进行研究。除出过多部诗集外,还写有以儿童为对象的小说和诗集。本书所选的《400 米自由泳》和后面一首《圣诞树》表明:一些现代诗人(当然古代也有)对诗行安排所构成的图形特别感兴趣(从本诗可看出,这"游泳池"是长度为 25 米的"短池",而这一点在诗的文字中是看不出来的)。

A. R. Ammons （1926— ）

生于北卡罗莱纳州,曾在加州大学学习理科。1964 年后移居纽约州中部城市伊萨卡,在当地的康奈尔大学任教。

William Burford （1927— ）

生于路易斯安那州,于阿默斯特学院毕业后,在约翰斯·霍普金斯大学获硕士及博士学位。曾在美国的多所大学任英语教授。本书所选的《圣诞树》与《400 米自由泳》有异曲同工之妙,可称为拟形诗、形象诗、像形诗、具体诗及圣坛诗(得名于十七世纪英国诗人赫伯特的作品《圣坛》,可参看上海译文版《英国抒情诗选》)。

Sylvia Plath （1932—1963）

生于德裔家庭,自幼即显露文学天赋,1955 年获得优厚奖金赴英留学。于剑桥大学毕业后与英国诗人 Ted Hughes（可参看《英国抒情诗选》）结婚,结果因感到生活痛苦而自尽。她死后却诗名大振,被认为是当代的杰出诗人。

后　记

英汉对照的拙译《英国抒情诗100首》于1986年出版后,几年间一再重印,并使我结识了不少热情的读者和同好(包括这次蒙其慨允,为本书作注的前辈译家俞亢咏先生)。这些都使我深受鼓舞,决意将早已酝酿的本书献给读者。

本书的出版虽因种种原因距上述姐妹篇较久,但编选的目的依旧。为了能同样得到对英语、对诗歌、对翻译等方面有兴趣的广大读者的喜爱,本书也编得略有系统,也有较充分的注释。同时,为力求有新鲜感,本书在尽量避免与拙译《美国抒情诗选》内容重复的前提下,同样做到既收文学史上有一定地位的诗家的名篇,也介绍我国读者尚不熟悉的诗人的佳作;既着重选取思想内容上积极健康、雅俗共赏的诗,也注意吸收风格、题材、趣味、韵律上各有千秋的诗。但考虑到美诗与英诗的不同历史、读者的方便及版面的合理和美观,本书在编排、格式及所用的字体等方面作了些改动。具体的情况,读者可在阅读时发现,这里就不赘述了。

然而我感到,有一个问题倒是有必要谈一下的。《英国抒情诗100首》的很多读者已经发现拙译中有一种倾向,即在翻译格律诗时,对原作中主要诉之于听觉的音韵上的格律,往往在尽可能将其转化为汉译中相应格律的同时,译文还构成一种有规则的图形,"体现"出格律。如果说这是一种特色或风格,那么在本书中这种倾向已变得更加明显,更加突出。然而这不是为图形而图形,却是遵循一种译诗要求而自然得到的结果。根据这种要求,构成原作格律的三项基本要素应在译文中反映出来。下面请看《简明不列颠百科全书》中"诗"这一条目中的例子:①

I could not look on Death, which being known,
Men led me to him, blindfold and alone.

----

① 本诗作者为1907年诺贝尔文学奖得主吉卜林。在有的诗选中,本诗的标题为"懦夫",写的是一个因临阵脱逃之类的罪名而被处决的军人。

这互相押尾韵的两行诗都含十个音节,每行诗可划分成各含前轻后重两个音节的五个音步(音步是西方诗歌的一种节奏单位,在英语的格律诗中,音步大多由一个重读音节带一二个非重读音节构成,当然,除此之外,诗行还有其他的构成方式,例如本书中《智力是一种迷人的东西》即是纯粹以音节为准的)。这样的押韵、音节、音步情况,根据我的做法,可以译成:

> 我未能 | 正视 | 死神;| 人们 | 一觉察,
> 便蒙住 | 我眼睛,| 单送 | 我去 | 见他。

可以看出,原作中的韵式在译文中保留了下来,原作中每行的五个音步在译文中以五个顿反映,原作中每行的十个音节在译文中则都以十二个汉字相应。这样做的结果,使译文在反映原作内容与形式的同时,利用汉语中一个音节便是一个字的特点,使原作中音节数或音步数相同但书面长度不同的诗行,在译文中连书面长度都变得相同了。同样的道理,原作中音节数或音步数相异的诗行,在书面上虽未必都能显示出来,但如按上述要求译,效果就非常明显。请看美国诗人诺克斯写的一首《合作》(Co-operation):

> It ain't the guns nor armament,
> 　　Nor funds that they can pay,
> But the close co-operation,
> 　　That makes them win the day.
>
> It ain't the individual,
> 　　Nor the army as a whole,
> But the everlasting teamwork
> 　　Of every blooming soul.

这首分成两节的短诗中,奇数行都是八音节构成的四音步;偶数行都是三音步,大多由六音节构成,唯一的例外是第六行,这里是七个音节,头三个音节构成一个音步。也就是说,这仍是一首格律很严谨的诗。对于这首诗,拙译为:

　　并不是靠枪炮或者军火，
　　　　不是靠拥有的财力，
　　而是靠紧密无间的合作，
　　　　他们才赢得了胜利。

　　靠的并不是一位位个人，
　　　　也不是军队这整体，
　　靠的是每个奋发的灵魂
　　　　持久的配合与协力。

　　可以看出,译文中以十字构成的四顿应原作的四音步,以八字构成的三顿应原作的三音步。这样,音节或音步数相同与相异的诗行(这里还包括互相押韵的相关诗行)可分得清清楚楚,使人一目了然,而且错落有致,变化有序。

　　当然上面这些都是最简单的例子,在译诗实践中遇到的情况可能要复杂些。[①] 但是凭上述例子,我感到已足可说明两点:

　　1) 多数英语格律诗的特征既然是以一定数量的音节构成一定数量的节奏单位(音步),那么在译文中以一定数量的字(音节),构成与原作音步数相等的汉语节奏单位"顿",自然是有依据的,也自然是合理的。

　　2) 由于我国读者未必都很熟悉英语诗歌的格律,特别是,由于以现代汉语写格律诗的情况也比较少见,因此,对一位普通的读者来说,要一眼就看出译诗是否有格律,有什么样的格律,恐怕是不太可能的。然而用上述兼顾字数、顿数及韵式的要求翻译,译文的书面形式就明白无误地显示出译文及原作格律上的特点。再说,格律诗中有规则的格律是其音乐性的体现,而反映在书面上,就自然比较整齐美观。

　　有了上述的合理性以及随之而来的有实际意义的图形性,还有一个可行性如何的问题。对此,我想单是本书中的一些格律诗也许已可说明:在翻译它们时,兼顾音节数(即字数)与顿数是做得到的,而且在某些情况下是必须顾到字数的,例如《智力是一种迷

---

① 对这个问题有兴趣的读者可参阅拙文《一种可行的译诗要求》、《从英语"像形诗"的翻译谈格律诗的图形美问题》及《译诗者与原诗作者的一次"对抗"》、《英语爱情诗一百首·前言》及《英诗格律的演化与翻译问题》(分别载《中国翻译》1992 年第 5 期、《外国语》1991 年第 6 期及 1993 年第 2 期与第 4 期及 1994 年第3 期)。

人的东西》、《400 米自由泳》、《圣诞树》等。

　　当然,译诗的根本要求还在于内容是否忠实于原作。而我限于本身的条件,很难指望在理解原作、汉语表达等方面没有这样那样的欠缺。我希望,英汉对照的出版形式,不仅有助于说明这类欠缺并非我这种译诗要求所必然造成的,也有助于读者进行多方面的比较,让译诗中的欠缺充分暴露出来。

　　　　　　　　　　　　　　　　　　　　黄杲炘
　　　　　　　　　　　　　　　　　　1993 年元月

图书在版编目（ＣＩＰ）数据

美国抒情诗100首: 英汉对照／黄杲炘编译.—上海:
上海译文出版社，1994. 10 (2001. 4 重印)
ISBN 7-5327-1537-X

I. 美 ... II. 黄 ... III. 英语－对照读物，诗歌－英、
汉 IV. H 319.4: I
中国版本图书馆 CIP 数据核字（2000）第 51653 号

美国抒情诗100首
（英汉对照）
黄杲炘 译
俞亢咏 注
世纪出版集团
上海译文出版社出版、发行
上海延安中路 955 弄 14 号
全国新华书店经销
上海出版印刷有限公司
开本 850 × 1168 毫米 1/32 印张 11.25 字数 309,000
1994 年 10 月第 1 版 2001 年 4 月第 2 次印刷
印数: 5,001-8,100 册
ISBN7-5327-1537-X/H·285
定价: 15.20 元